ROUGH DIAMONDS

A PRACTICAL GUIDE

NIZAM PETERS
AUTHOR

American Institute of Diamond Cutting, Inc.
Phone: U.S. (800)831-8470 toll free
Foreign (954) 574-0833
www.roughdiamonds.com
email:diamondcutting@worldnet.att.net

Publisher: American Institute of Diamond Cutting, Inc.
Ft. Lauderdale, Florida U.S.A.

Library of Congress Catalog Card Number: 98-74797

ISBN 0-9665854-1-0

Acknowledgment

I would like to express my thanks to all the people that have helped and assisted in the completion of this needed work.

Without the help and assistance of Mrs. Kimberly Hanna Stanley this work would not have been possible. She has laboriously typed the initial text, drafted and redrafted my numerous corrections. Countless times she has reformatted the pages of this work on her computer so that the text could be presented in an orderly and concise manner to the reader.

Mrs. Stanley is a graduate of the American Institute of Diamond Cutting and an accomplished diamond cutter. She is versed in all aspects of diamond manufacturing and is an instructor at the Institute. Her computer skills combined with her diamond knowledge has given her a leading edge in the diamond industry. She looks forward to continue serving the industry and break new ground in the furtherance of quality education.

Many thanks to my wife Robin for her helpful suggestions and hard work in completing the necessary corrections in a timely manner.

My friend Mr. Fernando Gomez was instrumental in the publication of this work. My thanks for his language skills and persistence in producing a quality publication.

Cover photograph – *A parcel of gem quality rough diamonds from South America.*

Disclaimer

Dedicated to

Shikira Peters

Leslie Peters

Jacob Peters

INTRODUCTION

Rough diamonds is an area in which very little written material can be found and at best is insufficient to gain any useful information. Those within the industry that are privileged to have this knowledge through trial, error and hard fought experience are hesitant in sharing, thus perpetuating the ignorance that already exist.

The information and conclusions presented in this work are from the authors observations from dealing with rough diamonds and from the perspective of cutting and polishing the rough over a period of twenty eight years. It is hoped that the reader will use this work as a stepping stone to further educate himself by seeking practical training before going into the field.

To be able to grade any single piece of rough or an entire parcel, one must be able to understand the following:

(a) The shape and structure of the rough.

(b) The surface features and internal growth.

(c) Internal and external inclusions and their location.

(d) The color of the rough and its influence both internally and externally.

When combining the above four basic categories in the right combination, one can then intellectually extract what the rough will yield after it is cut and polished. Only then can one begin to think in terms of what price to affix to the rough diamond. To seek rough prices from a preprinted rough price sheet is like saying, all vehicles that are blue in color, have the same price.

In the past there were only two general categories of rough diamonds.

(a) Gem quality

(b) Industrials

Rough diamonds are now categorized in three broad classifications.

(a) Gem quality rough

(b) Near gem quality rough

(c) Industrial rough

Because of advance manufacturing methods and quantities of borderline rough diamonds that are entering the market, it would be more practical to think in terms of:

(a) Cuttable rough diamonds (Gem)

(b) None cuttable rough diamonds (Industrials)

The varieties in which cuttable rough diamonds occur is indeed vast, compounded with this is the present ability to manipulate the rough to extract the best quality with the greatest amount of weight through a variety of cutting styles and new technology. Since this is the first work if its kind, many new words never before used will have to come into existence to describe in an understandable manner certain areas of discussion. The author's intention is to keep this work free from cumbersome technical language and present an educational format that will be easily understood by anyone.

CONTENTS

CHAPTER ONE

OVERVIEW OF THE ROUGH DIAMOND MARKET

OVERVIEW OF THE ROUGH DIAMOND MARKET

1. MINING

A. Diamond deposits

Diamonds are economically recovered generally from two sources.

(a) Primary deposits.

These types of deposits are located deep within the earth's crust in which the diamonds are moved towards the surface by kimberlite or lamproite.

(b) Secondary Deposits

This is where the diamonds were transported by rivers and their tributaries from their original source. Weathering and erosion also assist in the movement of diamonds from one location to the other.

When diamonds are found in river beds, these are referred to as alluvial deposit. In some cases the diamonds are found in old dried up riverbeds. Diamonds that are transported either on shore or offshore are referred to as marine deposits and can be found on the shoreline or at varying depths under the sea floor.

From the above two deposits, secondary deposits were known and worked first because of their relative ease in being accessible to miners.

B. Prospecting

Prospecting is seeking or searching for mineral deposits. We can briefly look at the three progressive aspects of prospecting.

(a) Original or traditional prospecting.

In traditional prospecting a prospector packed his tools over his back or pack animal and set out to look for diamonds either in the river or along the river bank. His main tools included a pick, shovel, pan, knife, rifle and other small tools. Food sources in most cases consisted of hunting or fishing. The area chosen to prospect would first be sampled and if it looked promising further extensive work would be done. The work was extremely difficult and labor demanding with the added drawback of battling the elements. Today in most of the underdeveloped countries, this type of prospecting still exists. Added to the harsh conditions is the modern day pressure from government authorities to obtain and maintain mining and prospecting permits.

(b) Scientific or educated prospecting.

The land is surveyed in a general way to glean a pattern or set of ideas leading to the conclusion of the possibility of diamonds being more abundant in one area than the other. The type and nature of the deposits in which the diamonds are found is then used to locate its possible original source or other similar type conditions. This can be particularly difficult because of the constant changing terrain. The diamonds can be traced to certain rivers and tributaries, old dried up riverbeds ranging in different depths underground as well as compact hard pipes in which the rock will have to be blasted loose.

(c) Hi-tech prospecting.

Diamonds are usually found in remote inaccessible areas, however a shifting of the population to new areas with road and small airport accessibility has brought the prospector to a closer proximity to diamond bearing areas.

The larger mining companies with huge capital at their disposal are able to avail themselves of modern technical equipment. Infrared aerial photography electro magnetic mapping are commonly used to map vast areas in a matter of hours. All of this is coordinated by computer and potential mining areas are deduced.

C. Recovery

The process of recovering diamonds are diverse and varied. They range from very primitive to extremely hi-tech. Most of the underdeveloped countries in which alluvial mining occurs, the same recovery methods for the past one hundred years have generally remained the same. Before recovery can commence a sampling of the area is first established. This procedure is used to locate the area in which the saturation of diamonds are highest. Normally this will be the first area to commence work. Sampling generally consist of two types.

(a) The first is in which a pit, hole or trench is dug to varying depths to reach the diamond bearing gravel (alluvial), yellow ground or blue ground. The gravel or blue ground is removed, washed and sorted to extract any diamonds that exist. Repeating this method from area to area, it is then compared to other samples and a choice is made as to whether it is better to work one area over another.

(b) The second method of sampling is done by using an auger. (Similar to that of a drill bit) A support arm is used to turn the auger into the ground and a sample is extracted to be washed and sorted. The samples are compared and a decision is made as to which area would be the most practical to work first.

Marine or sea sampling is done in much the same way as the above. Holes are placed by means of a drill on the seabed in which samples are extracted. The entire drill system is mounted on a ship fully equipped to wash and sort the samples as well.

With today's modern technology, the information from the diamonds that were extracted from the samples, are fed into a computer along with the size, color and clarity to determine the viability of mining in one area over another.

The actual recovery of diamonds from an area that is deemed productive usually has the same objective. To obtain as much diamonds as possible with a minimum loss of diamonds during washing and of course with a minimum amount of effort. The following are two general recovery descriptions.

(a) In alluvial river deposits the gravel is either washed in a pan or circular sieves by twirling it in a mixture of water and collected gravel. The diamond being heavier than its host material will collect in the center of the pan or sieve and then be removed.

Another popular method is one in which the gravel is sucked up and dumped on a set of riffles. The riffles are a set of square metal grids that are set at an angle to collect the gravel as it is washed across its surface. Many other methods are used to extract the diamonds from the gravel and sand, various types of which are employed depending on the variety of sand gravel and rock that is encountered. The above methods are still employed by individual miners in the underdeveloped countries.

(b) The pipe mine or ground mine which consist of diamond-bearing rock that is broken up through blasting and other methods, goes through a different process to extract the rough diamonds as compared to your typical alluvial deposits. A popular method for collecting the rough diamonds was the grease tables with a rotating belt in which the crushed diamond bearing rock is washed over a layer of grease. Diamonds have an affinity for grease and will adhere to it, the grease is then collected and boiled to separate the diamonds. Other methods include treatment plants for very large operations as well as heavy media separators. There are numerous other separation processes that are utilized. The most widely used are x-ray separators and optical separators. The former uses x-ray as a means of separation and the latter is used as a double check system during other methods of separation.

Different deposits offer unique challenges in extracting the rough diamond. Depending on where the diamond is found, under the seabed or in frozen ground, both mining and extracting the diamond produce their own special obstacles to overcome.

2. CLASSIFICATION.

Rough diamonds fall in a wide variety of sizes, shapes, color and clarity. They can be sorted or divided in individual groups of similar types. As market conditions change new categories are developed on diamonds. Rough diamonds that previously fitted into one group can be shifted into another. Large single diamonds are examined and graded on an individual basis. The following general classification can be assigned to rough diamonds coming directly from a mine.

(a) Gem quality rough diamonds

(b) Near gem quality rough diamonds

(c) Industrial quality rough diamonds

We will examine each separately and again this will be done on a general basis.

(a) **Gem Quality** - These diamonds consist of both large and small rough and represents the highest prices per carat in value of each of the three categories. The shapes of these diamonds are more uniform than the other two categories and will yield a higher weight retention of finished product than the near gem category. This type of rough diamonds are usually transparent with shinny to slightly dull matted surfaces.

(b) **Near Gem Quality** In the past much of the diamonds in this group were considered for industrial use. However, due to new technology in manufacturing and a significant lowering of quality in the marketplace a high proportion of diamonds obtained from the mines are now manufactured for sale in jewelry. Any portion of industrial diamonds that have some degree of transparency and can be extracted by cleaving, sawing or lasering is removed and processed. A large percentage of near gem is returned to the industrial category after portions for gem quality manufacturing is removed. Undesirable colors, especially in the brown range, are also manufactured and promoted in jewelry.

6

(c) **Industrial Quality** - Diamonds that fall in this classification are nearly always non-transparent and usually without a uniform shape. Although a high percentage from certain mines conforms to a cube or cuboid shape. Industrial diamonds range in all colors from colorless to varying shades of yellow, green, gray, brown and black. They are graded primarily for sizes. Their use in the industry is wide and varied with new application being discovered and applied as fast as technology changes.

In view of the above three classifications, it would probably be more accurate to combine the three classes and view them broadly according to the following.

(a) Cuttable Rough Diamonds (Gem)

This designation would separate all rough diamonds that could be manufactured into a category of present day standard of finished grading that would ultimately be mounted in a piece of jewelry. We would have to bear in mind that when cuttable material is extracted from borderline rough the remaining portion is put in the non- cuttable category.

(b) Non-Cuttable Rough Diamonds (Industrial)

This designation would take into account all rough diamonds that do not have a suitable quality when manufactured and that would not ultimately fall into a class of finished grading. It would also include rough diamonds that are cut and polished to produce angle surfaces or edges for industrial use as well as those rough diamonds crushed into abrasive powder or grit for other uses.

Rough diamonds found in nature comes in such a wide variety of:

(a) Sizes
(b) Shape and structure
(c) Quality (internal and external)

(d) Color

Each rough diamond to be designated for manufacturing, regardless of size, must be inspected individually and multiple calculations made to arrive at a feasible purchase price. The manufactured shape and type of cut must also be factored in the purchase price as well. Each of the above main areas will be dealt with in an entire chapter separately.

3. PRODUCTION AND MARKETING

The production of rough diamonds continues to increase through new discoveries while the demand for rough both industrially and through the jewelry industry, has kept pace with increased production. However the area of production and marketing need to be examined independently for a true picture of global production and consummation.

A. Production

Most of the worlds rough diamond production is mined in seven countries, South Africa, Botswana, Zaire, Angola, Namibia, Australia and Russia. Traditionally 80% of most mined rough was considered industrial and 20% gem. When classifying in light of present day cuttable and non-cuttable categories, it is found that approximately half of all mined rough can be considered cuttable. However, it should be noted that mined rough diamonds in the one carat size that fall in the better area of color and clarity have remained the same even through mined production has increased appreciably.

As we look towards the future, the consumer markets will continue to expect from the mining companies a steady supply of gem quality diamonds. Therefore it is imperative that new deposits are discovered and bought to production levels. We are presently seeing new discoveries, which in all probability will be the new future sources for rough diamonds. Areas such as Northern Canada, Northern Russia, and off shore marine deposits. The marine deposits hold great surprises for the future.

8

B. Marketing

In the past, rough diamonds where sold and manufactured through a tight corporate circle. This traditional closed market is rapidly changing. Diamond manufactures are not only obtaining their rough from their regular sources in support of the overall market but they are also purchasing from any and all outside sources. Their margins of profit from outside purchases, needless to say, are much better than their regular sources. As a result this gives rise to an ever widening free market in rough. Another important factor that is occurring is one in which the manufacturer is bridging the gap between himself and the retailer by stepping over the wholesaler or middlemen and going directly to the retailer.

Another factor contributing to a new emerging market which is presently in the process of being played, is the quantity of near gem rough that does not have a firm support base. This will eventually play itself out in the market in which supply and demand will establish a realistic market price for near gem rough. Along with the above, consideration must be given to the quality of cut with regard to the grade quality of a diamond. Generally the better the quality of rough, a manufacturer will put a better cut whereas the lower the quality less attention is given to detail of cut. This has given rise to a two tier market of inexpensive mass marketed diamond jewelry and a much higher priced quality oriented diamond jewelry to the consumer.

One of the single most important aspects of marketing the end product of a rough diamond is promotion. Advertising is not only done together as an industry but individually by countless retailers. As a result, world wide diamond jewelry consumption continues to increase from year to year and the foreseeable future.

Along with this is a distribution network of rough diamond dealers and manufacturers, which makes certain that diamonds are channeled in the right amount to the market needs and requirements. In the long run the market will remain stable and strong irrespective of the new changes that are taking place.

4. **PRICING AND VALUE**

To put a value on any single gem rough or parcel, it must be considered in relation to its size, shape, clarity, color and of course its ultimate shape and cut. Industrial rough diamonds on the other hand are considered in terms of size, shape and ultimate usefulness. Of course in terms of usefulness, this will change according to industry needs and use. Therefore, to grasp the concept of values in the diamond industry one needs to examine it from an overall perspective.

In todays global environment the gem rough diamond need to be understood to almost an exact science. One on one instruction with a qualified instructor who is well versed in the rough market is imperative to put together all the variables and options with respect to both purchase and marketing the rough diamond. The profit margins in many cases are narrow and therefore the lack of correct knowledge in planning the rough diamond to its final shape and weight can be an area of loss rather than profit. In the past, the purchase price of a rough diamond allowed a greater profit margin. However today, whether purchasing rough in a diamond bourse or deep in the amazon jungle, that profit margin is not as great. Armed with the correct knowledge and its application makes the difference in real profit. Mine output in the three general classifications equals to approximately 45% industrial, 40% near gem and 15% gem quality. When comparing the percentage of industrials in the past at approximately 80%, we see a considerable drop because of the relatively new area of classification in which we refer to as near gem. The reasons for the high proportional percentage of near gem is the advance of new technology in diamond manufacturing and the market consumption in lower quality diamond jewelry. When examining rough diamonds as a whole we also need to understand that ultimately the supply of finished diamonds in the market is controlled by the direct and indirect supply of rough diamonds through one or more agreed sources.

Other aspects to pricing is the cost factor during manufacturing and of course the cost of labor. Depending on these costs with the combined price of near gem and gem rough, this can easily create expensive finished diamonds if all areas are not considered from a purchase aspect of rough.

In the long term, diamond value will continue to rise with the assurance from the large producers that rough diamonds are not put onto the market at a rate that is greater in relation to what the market can consume. This keeps not only the supplier and consumer happy but all the middle areas such as the manufacturers, wholesalers and retailers.

The mechanics of pricing both gem quality rough and industrials are taught on a one on one basis in the rough diamond grading program at the American Institute of Diamond Cutting. (See chapter 7 on valuing rough diamonds)

CHAPTER TWO

ROUGH DIAMOND STRUCTURE, SHAPE AND ORIENTATION

ROUGH DIAMOND STRUCTURE, SHAPE AND ORIENTATION

1. THE STRUCTURE OF THE ROUGH.

Rough diamonds fall in the cubic or isometric system. This means that their atoms fall in an orderly, repetitive pattern. The internal arrangement express itself in a uniform geometric shape externally. These shapes are easily recognized in gem quality rough. The crystal structure of a diamond also affects its internal properties such as the way light passes through the diamond, its hardness as well as its density or weight. The diamond structure in many respects is unique to itself.

Within a rough diamond the chemical composition (carbon atoms) and the internal structure is basically the same in which it manifests itself in a recognizable outward shape. This external shape may repeat itself so often that we can refer to it as the predominant habit of that particular type of material. With rough diamonds, the most frequent habit the rough takes is an octahedral or any number of modified octahedral shapes. The remaining type of shapes in rough diamonds can vary widely and can assume a combination or a multiplicity of shapes. We will now examine the most frequently occurring shapes in gem quality rough diamonds.

2. COMMON SHAPES OF ROUGH GEM DIAMONDS.

CUBE
2.1

13

A.   Cube. So that we do not make a common mistake, let us clarify that even though diamonds do fall in the cubic or isometric system, it does not mean that gem quality rough diamonds form as a cube shape. It does occur in gem quality form occasionally but much more frequently in an industrial or non cuttable form. This means that its grain structure and internal clarity is not suitable to be manufactured into a saleable gem diamond. In photo 2.1 we see a cube diamond that is bounded by six square surfaces at 90 degrees to each other in which each face is joined by twelve ribs. Each of the cube surfaces on the rough can be modified in nature to be in a convex or concave shape, each rib can be rounded or flattened to the extent in which the cube shape would be difficult to recognize.

OCTAHEDRON
2.2

B.   Octahedron. The predominant habit of gem quality rough is the octahedral shape or a modification thereof. In photo 2.2 we can recognize a shape that has eight triangular surfaces and six points of which faces and points are connected and bordered by twelve ribs. The octahedron can at times be very symmetrically formed in which it can be referred to as a glassy. Another way to view the basic octahedron is that of two pyramids glued at their base. This shape produces the maximum weight retention when manufacturing round brilliants.

DODECAHEDRON
2.3

C.   Dodecahedron. Photo 2.3 is a typical shape of a dodecahedral form. It consist of twelve rhombic-shaped faces. From a manufacturing stand point it is treated exactly the same as an octahedron, therefore its weight retention for round brilliants is the same and in some cases two to three percent higher because of its bulged out shape. If we examine the dodecahedron carefully we will find the same six points that are found on the octahedron and therefore the relationship in many respects are the same.

WHOLE DIAMOND
2.4

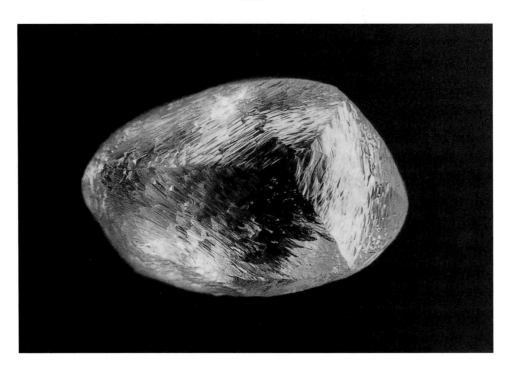

IRREGULAR DIAMOND
2.5

D. Whole and Irregulars. Rough diamonds that are modified with rounded faces and points with a thick or medium body and a semi circular outline are referred to as whole diamonds. If the shape is elongated it is considered an irregular.

In the three steps of manufacturing, sawing, brutting, cutting and polishing, whole and irregular rough does not go through the sawing process. Only one finished diamond is produced from the rough whereas with octahedrons and dodecahedron, two diamonds are obtained from each piece of rough. The weight retention from the whole and irregulars are less than sawed pieces. It should also be noted that whole diamonds (photo 2.4) are manufactured into rounds and irregulars and are frequently fashioned into fancy shapes. (photo 2.5)

CLEAVAGES
2.6

E.   Cleavages. This word applies to rough diamonds that have one or more broken surfaces that may or may not be in a cleavage direction. A cleavage break is located parallel to any given octahedral plane (face) irrespective of its outward form, once recognized it can be utilized to separate the rough in a number of areas if so desired.

17

The surface of a cleavage break is relatively smooth and transparent. Photo 2.6 is a typical rough diamond that is considered a cleavage. Its shape is usually irregular, triangular or semi rounded and nearly always flat.

FLATS
2.7

F.   Flats. This term is used to describe rough that is shallow with little or no body. In short the rough diamond does not have a depth ratio in relation to its width for manufacturing into a well made finished diamond. Photo 2.7 is a typical flat, these types of rough can often be triangular in shape to semi-rounded to elongated. Considerable loss of weight is encountered during manufacturing unless a modified cut is used. In some cases the flat is segmented through sawing or cleaving to produce smaller finished diamonds.

MACLE
2.8

G.   Macles. Photo 2.8 is a prime example of a rough macle. They are triangular in shape with the three sides being either straight or semi curved, the two opposite sides are typical octahedral faces. In the process of formation one of the faces literally rotated one hundred and eighty degrees with respect to the other. This creates a seam or line around the sides of the macle where the two faces meet. As a result, it is extremely difficult to manufacture this type of rough since the grain orientation is completely opposite to each other and does not run continuous in the entire rough. With the exception of a triangular cut, the weight retention of a macle is poor.

19

Some rough diamond may occur in combination forms. Following are two typical combination forms.

TWIN ROUGH
2.9

H.   Twin Rough. Additional to the preceding described diamonds, a rough may look perfectly normal but internally it is disoriented to the point in which its grain direction runs contrary to each other. Depending on the extent of the internal distortion of the growth patterns this rough may offer great difficulty during manufacturing. Examining photo 2.9 we can just recognize the slight change in the outward shape which indicates the difference in the internal formation.

CONTACT TWIN
2.10

I. Contact Twins. Another variety with the same type of phenomena but being quite distinct is contact twin rough. As shown in photo 2.10, we see two separate diamonds joined together at a common junction. This can occur with two or more distinct rough diamonds that are joined together to create a whole. The point at which they contact each other results in growth patterns and grain directions that is unique to each separate piece. Again, this will cause extreme difficulty in manufacturing and of course considerable weight loss.

3. ORIENTING THE ROUGH FOR WEIGHT RETENTION AND YIELD.

It should be understood that the single most important factor in weight retention is the shape in which the rough diamond is found. Its ultimate cut determines the final weight. Additional factors in the weight yield of a rough diamonds is its color and inclusions both internal and external. Inclusions particularly will affect the orientation of the rough diamond during manufacturing and ultimately the final weight yield of the rough. The combination of shape, inclusions, color and final cut can only be studied in a classroom environment which is equipped with an extensive variety of rough diamonds and studied on a one on one basis with a qualified instructor.

We will presently examine the most frequently encountered shapes of rough and their final weight retention and the reasons for their ultimate cut. (Note: To presently include the area of color and clarity, will make this study too complex, each of these areas will be studied in a separate chapter.)

A. Octahedrons and Dodecahedrons. These shapes are the most commonly encountered in rough gem diamonds and represent approximately 50% of rough diamond in a typical parcel. They have a regular consistent form which allows the cutting and polishing of two round brilliants.

They are frequently referred in the manufacturing industry as sawables. Photo 2.11 reveals a sawed octahedron. The two pieces are ideally suited for fashioning into two round brilliants. Each piece is rounded on the bruting machine bringing it to a circular outline as shown in photo 2.12. After bruting, cutting and polishing, each piece will yield 50% of its original weight. A dodecahedron that goes through the same procedure will yield at times as much as 55% or more weight. To plan octahedrons and dodecahedrons in any other way, other than sawing, will yield weight retention of much less that 50%.

SAWED OCTAHEDRON
2.11

BRUTED DIAMOND
2.12

Octahedrons and dodecahedrons, after sawing, can also be fashioned into square princess cuts, or radiant, barion and step cut emerald when rectangular in shape. Sawing octahedrons and dodecahedrons in half is not the only option in dividing these types of rough. Off center sawing or topping can be a viable alternative especially when the rough diamond will yield finished weights in desirable weight classes, such as over .50ct or 1.00ct. etc....

B.   **Whole and Irregulars.** Both whole and irregular diamonds are fashioned into one single finished diamond. Whole rough diamonds with a circular outline will yield a 45% weight recovery while those with a slightly elongated outline will produce a finished weight of approximately 40%. An irregular shape in which the outline is elongated, can easily conform to any number of fancy shapes. Weight retention is usually 40% to 45% especially when the outline of the irregular rough is best suited to the specific cut. If the cutter insists on fashioning a round brilliant when the rough shape is more desirable for a fancy cut, the weight loss can be in excess of 70%. It is important that the orientation of the whole and irregular shapes conform to a specific width to depth ratio that will be in relation to each other. (photo 2.13) In other words if the diameter of the rough is not proportional to its depth, the proportions of the diamond will be poor and an excessive amount of weight can be lost.

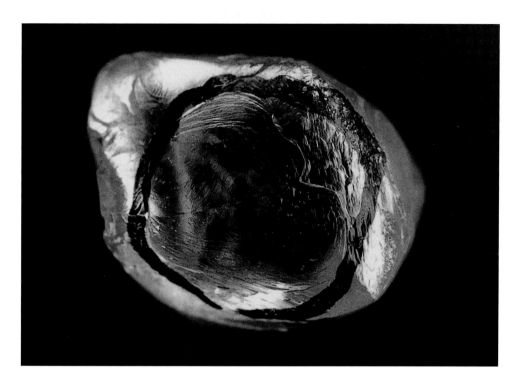

**MARKED ROUND WHOLE DIAMOND
2.13**

C.   Cleavages. As we have seen before, these are rough diamonds that have one or more broken surfaces or areas. Their shape can be irregular, uniform or with straight parallel or tapered sides. The final cut in which these types of rough lend themselves can range from round brilliants and fancy shapes as well as straight and tapered baguettes. The weight retention during manufacturing will range from 25% to 40%.

D.   Flats.. These types of rough diamonds inherently produces a low weight yield because of their less than ideal depth percentage. The rough when manufactured will usually produce finished diamonds with shallow proportions in both round and fancy shapes. The weight yield will fluctuate from 20% to 35% for round brilliants and 25% to 42% on fancy cuts.

E.   Macles. By the very shape of rough macles, it is easy to visualize a triangular cut. They are frequently manufactured in this type of cut because of the average 45% weight retention when finished. Macles that are flat without sufficient depth, will have a weight retention of 30% to 40% providing a triangular cut is used. The type of triangular cut that is frequently used today is a modified brilliant cut for both the crown and pavilion. If a round brilliant cut is used on the macle, the weight retention is usually 35%.

It should be remembered that the largest and flattest area on the rough diamond is usually used to grind the table facet. The diameter of the rough should be proportionate to its depth. Without establishing a reasonable ratio of the two measurements, the diamond can easily have poor proportions or too great of a weight loss. This area of planning the rough is extremely important and will be examined in detail during the rough diamond grading class at A.I.D.C. Inc.

CHAPTER THREE
SURFACE FEATURES

SURFACE FEATURES

GENERAL. The surface of a diamond can vary considerably from one crystal to the other. The outer surface texture can indicate the type of deposit the diamonds originated from and the different conditions that may have existed during its process of formation. Surfaces range from transparent to opaque in which inclusions can be readily hidden from observation. Understanding how surface features affect diamonds and one's ability to interpret it with regard to clarity and color is essential to be able to evaluate the rough diamond. This chapter will consider the surfaces of the diamond as it relates to surface clarity only. Surface features can be divided into two general categories.

      1. External surfaces features

      2. Near surface features

We will examine each area with their subclassifications as follows.

1. EXTERNAL SURFACE FEATURES.

These surfaces can be divided into four subclassifications:

      A. Mirror or glasslike surfaces

      B. Frosted or waterworn surfaces

      C. Grooved or serrated surfaces.

      D. Blemished surfaces.

      A. Mirror or glasslike surfaces. These types of surfaces can be found in all varieties of rough diamond shapes. Photo 3.1 reveals a group of transparent octahedrons and photo 3.2 a macle with a mirror surface. When the shape of the rough takes the form of a uniform octahedron with flat octahedral faces, defined ribs and a mirror finish, it is referred to as a glassy. This can be viewed in photo 3.3. These surfaces can also exist on only certain parts of the rough diamond in one or more locations. Diamonds with mirror or glasslike surfaces are frequently found with trigons. (See supplement at the end of subclassification A for detailed photographs on trigons. page 33)

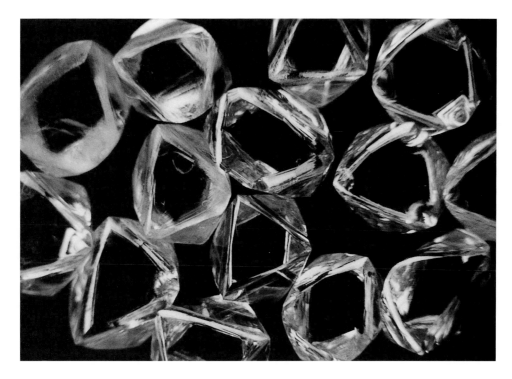

3.1

3.2

3.3

3.4

3.5

We can observe in photo 3.4 and 3.5 partial transparent surfaces on the rough. Glasslike or mirror like surfaces allows the greatest visibility within the rough diamond. Those surfaces that allow a partial view are sufficient to give the trained observer the necessary information to deduce overall internal clarity.

3.6

3.7

3.8

Trigons- (Supplement to subclassification A) Trigons are growth features that can often be observed on rough diamond surfaces. They can occur as single large triangular shapes (photo3.6), multiples of small trigons (photo 3.7), indented (photo3.8) or protruding from the surface. These growth marks are nearly always oriented 180 degrees to any of the given octahedral faces.

B. Frosted or waterworn surfaces. These type of surfaces are fairly common on rough diamonds especially those mined in alluvial deposits. They usually exist on non-octahedral and irregular rough. The surface is sometimes referred to as a sandblasted finish. These types of surfaces can easily hide inclusions (See section 2 of this chapter - near surface features) Photo 3.9 exhibits a group of frosted diamonds with varying degrees of transparency.

3.9

3.10

Photo 3.10 reveals a pitted type of frosted surface. The visibility within the diamond is practically nonexistent.

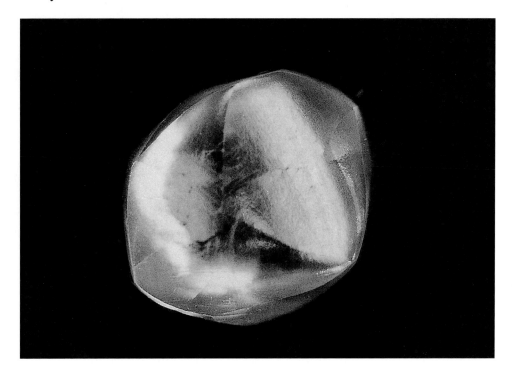

3.11

The rough diamond in photo 3.11 has a very smooth frosted surface, visibility can be accessed through certain sections when viewed under the correct lighting conditions.

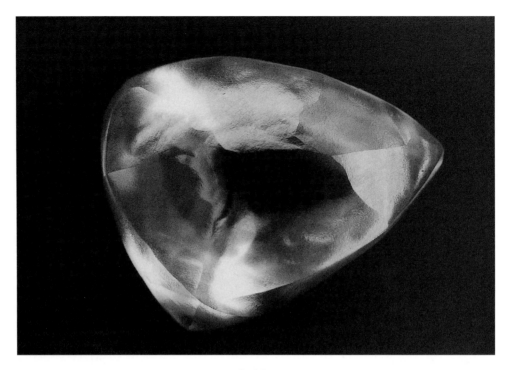

3.12

Even though this macle in photo 3.12 is frosted, the transparency is very good because the surface is lightly frosted and allows easy viewing under magnification.

3.13

Photo 3.13 is a rounded dodecahedron revealing another frosted surface similar to that of a sandblasted finish.

3.14

Before planning a rough diamond for manufacturing, especially if the surface is frosted, a window (small facet) is polished on the surface as shown in photo 3.14 to reveal any inclusions on the inside. As many windows as necessary can be polished on the rough diamond to assist in the examination.

C. Grooved or serrated surfaces. These are surfaces on rough diamonds that show growth lines (grain lines), wavy textured surfaces, step like and pitted surfaces. Surfaces such as these come from all types of deposits. The degree of internal visibility will range from clearly seeing internally to a view that may be completely obstructed on the entire rough surface.

3.15

Photo 3.15 reveals a grooved or growth layering along the ribs of the octahedron.

3.16

A wavy textured surface is seen in photo 3.16

3.17

This type of graining or wavy textured surface is frequently encountered in rough diamonds as shown in photo 3.17

3.18

A serrated step like surface is often encountered on rough diamonds as observed in photo 3.18.

3.19

We can observe in photo 3.19 another type of wavy textured appearance.

3.20

The macle in photo 3.20 reveals grooved or distinct grain patterns. It is also obvious that the surface is frosted and allows very little visibility within the rough diamond.

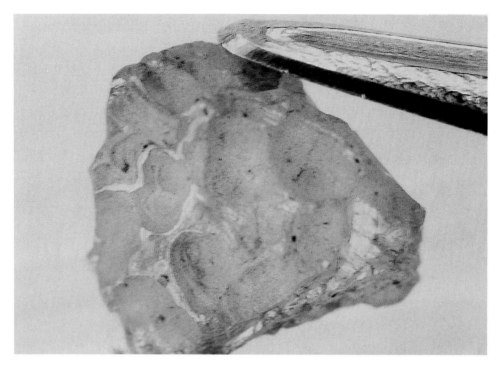

3.21

Photo 3.21 displays an unusual crater like surface that prohibits any type of examination internally.

3.22

Photo 3.22 is another unusual surface feature in gem quality rough. We can clearly see both a frosted and partially serrated surface with signs of growth layering. Internal visibility is non-existent.

Any of the described surfaces can occur as a combination of two or more surfaces on any single rough diamond.

Note: Understanding how to examine the surfaces of rough diamonds and their expected result after manufacturing will need to be taught on a one on one level with a professional instructor that has a diamond cutting and polishing background.

D. Blemished Surfaces. These type of surface features would include radiation stains and surface coating. They can be located on part of the rough or cover the entire surface. They can exist on both transparent and frosted surfaces. The color of radiation stains are normally green but they can also have varying degrees of brown color or a combination of the two.

3.23

43

Photo 3.23 reveals radiation stains in the form of minute spots covering the entire surface of the diamond. These types of radiation spots can sometime be mistaken for internal inclusions.

3.24

Photo 3.24 is a magnified view of photo 3.23 giving us a closer examination of the radiated surface.

3.25

Radiation stains can cover the entire diamond to the extent in which the rough can look completely black on the outer surface as seen in photo 3.25.

3.26

45

We can observe in photo 3.26 the partially processed diamond with part of the rough surface intact with the radiation stains. This clearly reveals that radiation stains are either strictly on the surface or very close to the surface.

3.27

Photo 3.27 reveals two radiation spots on the surface of this rough. They are the two darker spots. The other spots are internal carbon inclusions. It is very easy to mistake the two radiation spots as inclusions.

2. NEAR SURFACE FEATURES. There are five general subclassifications.

    (A) Hairline inclusions
    (B) Surface twinning
    (C) Fractured and cleaved surfaces
    (D) Extended surface inclusions-minor
    (E) Coated diamonds

Note: Each of the above subclassifications can be considered as internal inclusions in which they are either on the surface or break the surface of the rough. In other words near surface features exist from the surface and can extend slightly under the surface. When they become too numerous and of a size to become major inclusions, we will then define them further in chapter four. However, we will presently examine these type of inclusions when they are minor, hence the designation, "Near surface features."

A. Hairline inclusions. These are feather type inclusions that can exist on or close to the surface of the rough diamond. They can also exist well within the rough and will be considered under major inclusions. In most cases the hairline inclusions on the surface will usually be cut away during the process of manufacturing.

3.28

Photo 3.28 is a typical frosted surface on a modified octahedron. The rough surface looks relatively normal. (See also photo 3.29)

3.29

Photo 3.29 is a magnified view of the rough shown in photo 3.28. We can clearly observe the numerous hairline inclusions existing on the surface and extending slightly under the surface.

B. Surface twinning. The effects of twinning presents us with a twofold problem when we analyze the rough diamond. First, the area where the twinning occurs creates a seam in which after cutting and polishing usually remains on the polished surface of the diamond. This, in many instances, can cause a lowering of the clarity grade. Additionally, great difficulty is encountered due to cross grains during cutting and polishing. Secondly, many twinned areas found in the rough can have a plane of inclusions running along the twinned plane. These inclusions can run close to the surface or deep within the rough. (Deep inner inclusions with advanced twinning will be examined in chapter 4).

3.30

A twin line running along the center portion of the rough is clearly seen in photo 3.30. On closer examination we can detect inclusion on the right and left of the twin line.

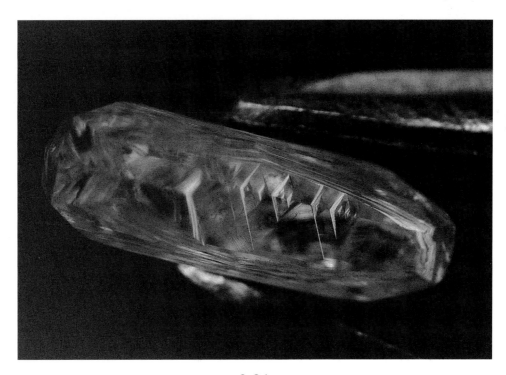

3.31

49

Photo 3.31 reveals a side view of a typical macle in which we can see obvious twinning running along the girdle plane. The twinning effect usually occurs on all three sides of the macle and at times may not be readily apparent.

C. Fractured or cleaved surfaces. This type of breakage normally occurs during the transportation of the rough diamond to the earth's surface and movement along the river beds. Cleaved surfaces occur along any given octahedral face and is usually a clean break. A fractured break is one that travels in any other direction other than along a cleavage plane. This type of break can be step like or fragmented. Additional inclusions can occur because of the break and they can travel well within the rough diamond.

3.32

Photo 3.32 displays a large cleaved surface on the rough. This type of break is clean and is strictly confined to the surface with very little or no internal damage.

3.33

Photo 3.33 reveals the front view of a fractured break. These type of breaks can frequently have small to major feather inclusions extending into the rough.

3.34

Photo 3.34 shows a conchoidal feature on the rough diamond. This is unusual to find, however it does occur in rare cases, contrary to popular teaching.

D. Extended surface inclusions-minor. Inclusions of this type can extend from the rough surface to shallow depths under the surface. (Inclusions that are deep within the diamond will be explored in chapter 4). Extended surface inclusions are usually removed during the cutting and polishing process. These inclusions usually consist of tiny feathers and small carbon spots. Careful examination with regard to the depth of the inclusion is required to judge the clarity grade of the rough before manufacturing.

3.35

We can observe a 2.90ct rough octahedron in photo 3.35 with two feather inclusions almost intersecting each other. The larger inclusion has a wider width and therefore is slightly deeper under the octahedral face. Both feather inclusions have an excellent possibility of being removed during cutting and polishing.

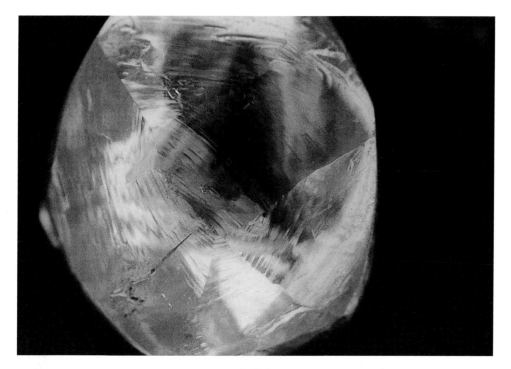

3.36

Photo 3.36 reveals a line feather inclusion at 8 0'clock (See also photo 3.37)

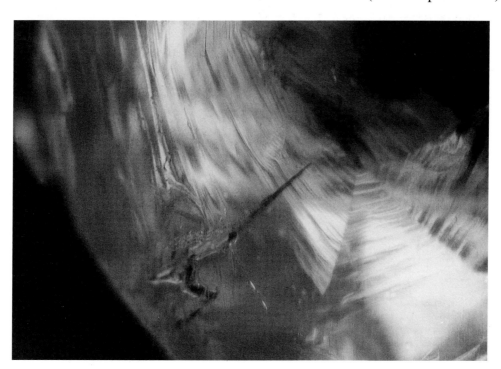

3.37

Photo 3.37 shows the same inclusion that was examined in photo 3.36 but under higher magnification. We can now deduce that it does not travel deep within the rough and will therefore be completely removed during manufacturing.

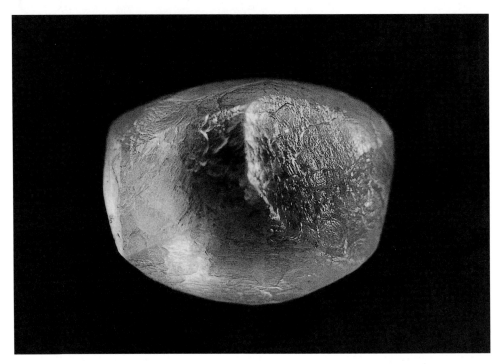

3.38

Photo 3.38 reveals another feather inclusion that not only covers 75% of the width of the rough but it also has relative depth. The location of this inclusion is on the largest surface area of the diamond which will probably accommodate the table facet. In this instance part of the feather inclusion may remain after manufacturing.

3.39

Observe a 2.37ct rough with various surface inclusions in photo 3.39. The open surface of the inclusions are filled with dirt which gives the illusion that the inclusions are worse than they really are. The surface inclusions are usually completely removed after cutting and polishing.

E. Coated diamonds. Rough diamonds of this type are usually opaque to semitransparent. The surface is coated with a skin that varies in thickness. The body within the rough is usually of a normal clarity and color range. It is extremely difficult to tell how deep the skin penetrates the rough surface. It may exist throughout the entire diamond, in which case the rough can only be considered for industrial use. The surface appearance shows the same growth patterns that exist in standard rough diamonds. However, the color of the coating or skin can range in various shades of gray, white, green, yellow, brown and black. In most cases the perceived color is a result of surface staining and or an abundance of microscopic inclusions that impart the surface color.

3.40

Photo 3.40 shows a 1.82ct rough with both the skin and transparent surface. Notice the thickness of the skin along the edges of the transparent surface.

3.41

Photo 3.41 reveals a 1.05ct rough that has an opaque surface, similar to a type that can be found on an industrial rough. Three facets have been cut, one to the left, right and base. (See also aerial view of photo 3.42)

3.42

Photo 3.42 is an aerial view of photo 3.41. Some transparency can be seen from the surface of the table facet through the two pavilion facets.

3.43

Photo 3.43 is a portion of the coated diamond that was observed in photo 3.41 and 3.42. Along the girdle edge one can see a portion of the original skin remaining in the finished diamond.

The technique in which each surface will need to be examined can only be taught on a practical basis with actual hands on examination of rough diamonds in the classroom under specialized supervision.

CHAPTER FOUR

INTERNAL FEATURES

INTERNAL FEATURES

OVERVIEW OF INTERNAL INCLUSIONS.

Internal inclusions can be viewed within the diamond depending on the transparency of the rough diamond surface. If the surface is not transparent enough, one or more windows can be polished to allow whatever observation may be necessary. Internal inclusions can range from dark to light colors or can be very transparent. The very dark inclusions can be seen as black in color to various degrees of transparency mixed with shades of brown to any number of additional colors. A combination of both dark and light inclusions can be found in rough diamonds. The greatest problem in detection is when the inclusions are transparent and blends with the body of the rough in a location that is not at first apparent.

During examination of any internal inclusion we need to look at it from two basic perspective.

(a)　　Size of the inclusions – Is it centrally located? Is it extending from the surface to the interior of the rough? Is the inclusion large enough and of a type that may cause the rough diamond to separate during any of the manufacturing processes.

(b)　　Position of the inclusion. Can the inclusion be removed during manufacturing based on the type of cut that will later be executed? If the inclusion is to be left in the finished diamond, can it be positioned in the crown facets or close to the girdle edge? This type of foresight can significantly improve the clarity grade.

Proportional analysis in relation to the location of internal inclusions will require supervision by a qualified instructor on a one on one basis to gain the necessary insight for purchasing in the field.

COMMON TYPES OF INCLUSIONS.

In the following pages we will examine the most frequently encountered internal inclusions and how they affect the rough diamond. These inclusions can occur in combination with each other, separately or with other varieties of inclusions. We will examine them in the following order.

1.　　Carbon (gray to black)
2.　　Feathers
3.　　Pinpoints (white)

4. Clouds
5. Advanced twinning
6. Stress and Strain

1.   Carbon Inclusions.   These inclusions come in various shades of gray to black and can be located anywhere in the rough diamond.   They range in size from tiny pinpoints, to groups of pinpoints to masses of large irregular shapes. Carbon inclusions are frequently encountered in rough diamonds.

4.1

Photo 4.1 reveals a single carbon inclusion in an irregular shape rough.

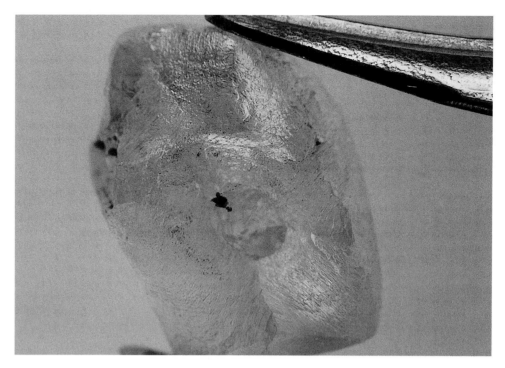

4.2

Photo 4.2 shows several carbon inclusions close to the surface of this rough diamond.

4.3

Photo 4.3 displays carbon inclusions grouped together in an irregular shape rough.

62

4.4

In photo 4.4 we can see a side view of the inclusion displayed in photo 4.3. Notice that the inclusions are closer to one of the larger faces and also the depth of inclusions can be observed from this view.

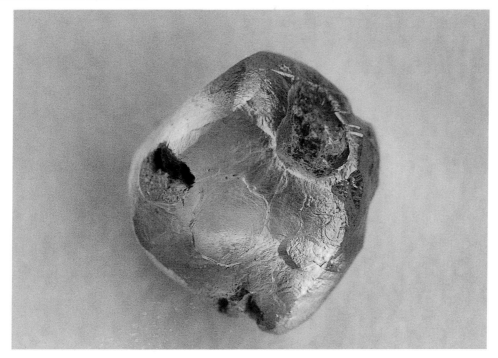

4.5

Photo 4.5 are of carbon inclusions that are close to the surface of the rough and, depending on the orientation during manufacturing, may easily be removed.

4.6

Looking through an octahedral face in photo 4.6, we can examine a group of pinpoint carbon inclusions.

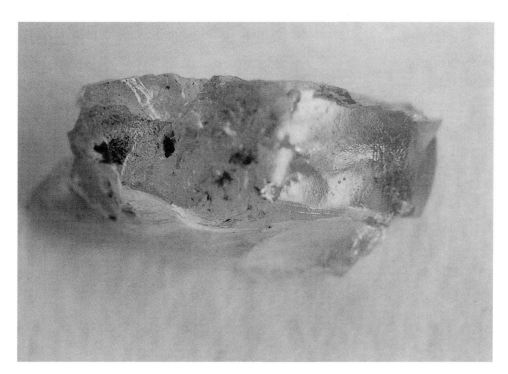

4.7

From a side view in photo 4.7 we can observe both single large carbon inclusions and pinpoint carbon inclusions.

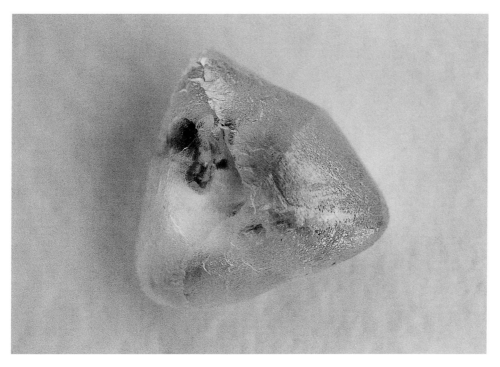

4.8

Photo 4.8 is a rough macle with large noticeable carbon inclusions. The light gray areas reveal additional carbon inclusions that are not obvious because of their depth. Viewing of these inclusions will be more visible from the opposite side of the rough.

4.9

Photo 4.9 shows major carbon inclusions when examined through one of the octahedral faces. (see also photo 4.10)

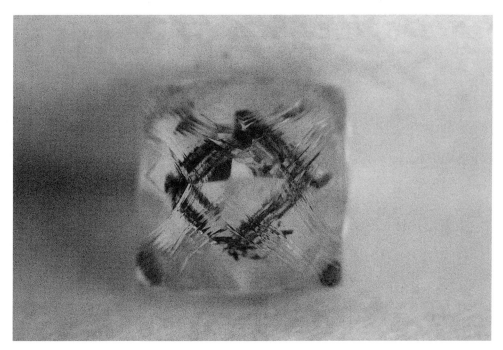

4.10

This is an aerial view of the same rough in photo 4.9. Observe in photo 4.10, a square shape reflection pattern that covers all four octahedral faces. In an octahedral rough, the eight faces can often act as a mirror depending on the location of the inclusion.

4.11

Photo 4.11 reveals the side view of a sawed rough. We can clearly see two of the carbon inclusions located just under the sawed plane. (see also photo 4.12)

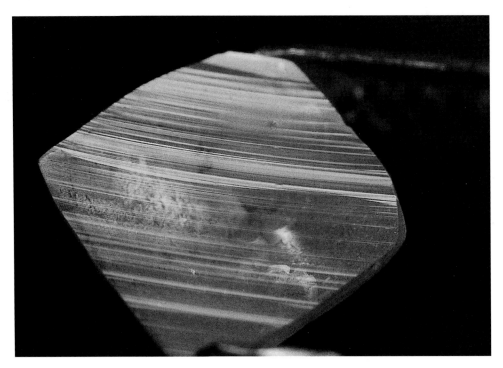

4.12

Photo 4.12 is an aerial view of photo 4.11. Observe the saw lines and the two carbon inclusions that were seen from the side, with a number of additional carbon pinpoints.

2.   Feather Inclusions. There are generally two types of feather inclusions, "Fracture feather and cleavage feathers". These are breaks that create a weakness within the structure of the rough diamond. Cleavage feathers or fissures can at times extend their depth or cause complete separation during the manufacturing of the rough. Cleavage feathers exist parallel to any cleavage plane and are the easiest division point on a rough diamond. Both cleavage and fracture feathers are white to transparent in appearance.

4.13

Photo 4.13 displays a feather inclusion running from one side of the rough to the opposite. This type of inclusion can easily extend further within the diamond during the manufacturing process. It can also cause a complete division of the rough.

4.14

Observe in photo 4.14, a large polished window on a 3.10ct rough in which we can see a large and small feather inclusion traveling along parallel planes.

4.15

Photo 4.15 reveals a magnified view of a dangerous feather inclusion originating from the rough surface and extending within the diamond.

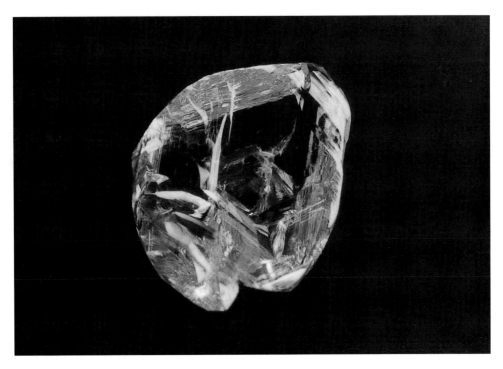

4.16

We can examine numerous feather inclusions in photo 4.16, which are situated on both sides of the macle.

4.17

Photo 4.17 shows a V type feather inclusion that extends slightly under the surface. (see also photo 4.18)

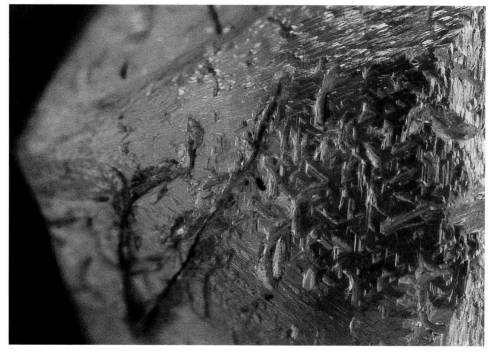

4.18

Photo 4.18 is a magnified view of the feather inclusions in photo 4.17. One can clearly see the open edge of the feather along the surface of the rough. Additionally, smaller feather inclusions with minimal depths are apparent on the surface. They radiate from the large feather inclusions.

3.   Pinpoints. The term pinpoints are given to tiny white inclusions, which can be solid or semi transparent within the diamond. They can occur as a single pinpoint or as a scattered group. They are the white counterpart to carbon pinpoints. Within the rough diamond they are difficult to detect because of the near colorless to colorless surface of the rough. At times the semi-transparent inclusions when observed under a microscope are found to be miniature rough diamond crystals.

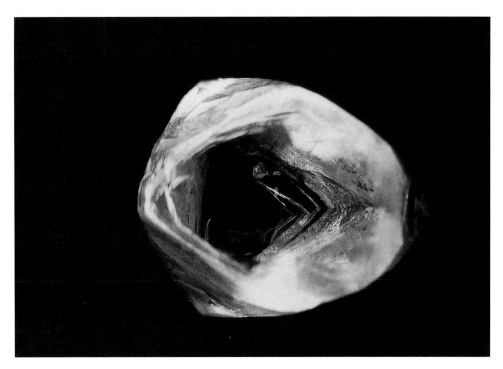

4.19

Photo 4.19 reveals a group of three white inclusions within the rough.

4.20

Centrally located, we can see a white group of inclusions in photo 4.20

4.21

Two transparent inclusions are revealed on the left middle area of the octahedral face in photo 4.21. These are miniature crystals within the rough.

4. **Clouds.** Usually when a group of white pinpoints become so numerous they are observed as a hazy effect within the diamond, the entire area is referred to as a cloud. As a general rule, clouds are very difficult to detect because of their foggy appearance. They can blend easily within the body of the rough diamond.

4.22

In photo 4.22 we can easily detect the clouded area within the rough diamond.

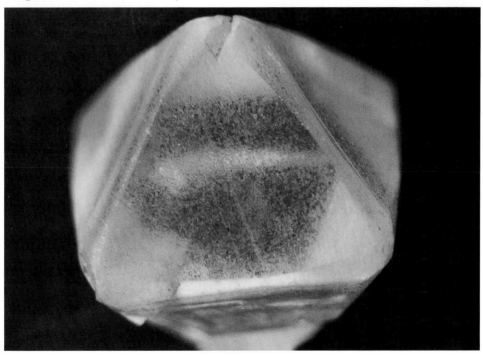

4.23

Photo 4.23 shows a clouded effect throughout the octahedron.

5.   Advanced twinning. This type of twinning does not only manifest itself on the surface but also deep within the diamond and usually exists from one side of the rough to the other. The grain structure or growth orientation on one or more sides of the rough is usually twisted contrary to the other. Along the plane of twinning any variety of inclusions may manifest themselves. A rough diamond that has advanced twinning is extremely difficult to cut and usually cannot retain a good polish. The clarity grade is usually at the lower end of the scale. Advance twinning can be a rough buyer's nightmare if he is not familiar with the many pitfalls.

4.24

We can clearly observe in photo 4.24 the twin plane that exists around this macle. Dark inclusions are also detected on the left side of the macle along the twin line. Notice how the grain forms a wide v shape pattern above and below the twin plane.

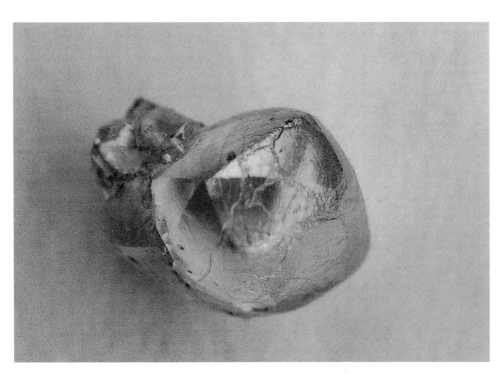

4.25

An attached protruded twinned area is visible on the left side of the rough in photo 4.25. Notice the darker areas at the junction in which the twinning occurs. This indicates inclusions well within the rough.

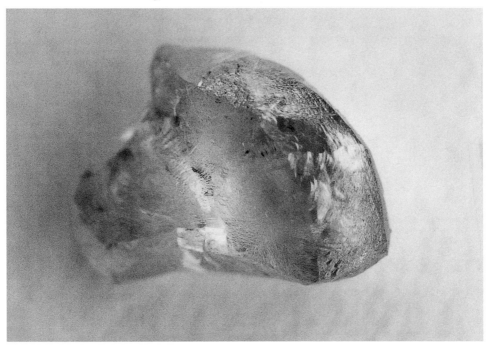

4.26

Photo 4.26 displays a twinned irregular rough with small dark inclusions throughout the diamond. The protruding area on the left is an outgrowth from the body of the rough.

4.27

Photo 4.27 is an aerial view of a macle. The unique pattern of carbon inclusions are all extending from the twinned middle area that exist around the macle.

4.28

Photo 4.28 reveals an example of intergrowth clearly showing the different grain directions that exist on the surface. There is great difficulty in manufacturing this type of rough.

4.29

In photo 4.29, a star shape is formed in this multiple twin rough. Notice the different patterns of interwoven grain directions.

6. **Stress and strain.** This is a condition within rough diamonds that is caused by either internal structural changes or the position and tension some inclusions may create. They may be visible or invisible under magnification. When visible they are often seen with the entire colors of the spectrum. Feather inclusions with any discoloring are often indicative of stress and strain. Brown colored diamonds generally have greater stress and strain than their colorless counterpart. Stress and strain can sometimes have enough tension within the rough in which the diamond can easily fracture during the manufacturing process. (We will examine this further in chapter six) Photo 5.33, 5.34 and 5.35 on page 105 and 106 in chapter five shows stress and strain in three rough diamonds.

CHAPTER FIVE

COLOR IN ROUGH

COLOR IN ROUGH

AN OVERVIEW OF COLOR. Understanding color in rough diamonds is more complex than examining finished diamonds for color. Claims of being able to accurately detect color in rough diamonds through an instrument are not presently feasible. The instrument will have to be capable of accounting for all the possible variables, such as:

a. Color that is caused other than by the body color of the rough such as the influence of a discolored inclusion.
b. Patches of color within the body that is not the same as the general body color.
c. Coated diamonds with one color on the surface and another internally.

It cannot be overstated that before the rough diamond buyer attempts a purchase in the field that making visual observations under controlled conditions with a qualified instructor is important to accurately observe color in rough diamonds. There is a great deal of additional influence that will need to be considered. This chapter will address only some of those issues with regard to color.

Examining color in rough diamonds means deciding how colorless is the rough or how deep a saturation of color does it have. The most common colors or non-colors encountered are from colorless to varying shades of gray, yellow and brown. Of course the exceptional colors are varying saturation's of blue, pink, green etc.... Before we address actual color in rough diamonds we need to be reminded of the following three areas.

1. **How to view color in rough.** When examining a rough diamond for color, it will need to be viewed against a white background, preferably a folded piece of white paper. The whiteness of the paper should be a neutral white, the same as used in general grading of finished diamonds. The angle for viewing is the same that is used for finished diamonds. The rough diamond should be turned and examined from several directions. Comparison rough diamonds can be used to define narrow ranges in color. Note: These comparison or master rough diamonds should be made up from the area in which future

rough diamonds will be purchased. A competent diamond cutter that is familiar with the result of color from the rough to the finished in that particular mining area is needed to put together a color comparison set.

2. Lighting conditions to view color. In an office environment standard daylight tubes are considered adequate lighting. The surrounding walls should be white or a neutral color. In the field, natural daylight is adequate under a shaded area such as under a tree or the overhang of a building. The rough diamond must never be viewed in direct sunlight, it is too strong of a light source and will mask the true color of the rough. Late in the evening and sunset light is not adequate light for color grading. Never color grade a rough diamond at night in a hotel room for obvious reasons.

3. Inherent influence. The rough diamond may have one or more factors that will influence the observed color, an obvious area is fluorescence. Colorless rough diamonds in particular that have strong fluorescence will cause the color to look better than it actually is. Rough diamonds that fluorescence strongly may impart a milky or hazy appearance to the rough. A number of other factors that influence rough diamond color are surface texture, inclusions etc. In the following pages we will examine the main areas individually.

HOW IS COLOR AFFECTED BY:

1.   Surface conditions. Rough diamond color can be affected not only by the surface texture but also by the type of pigments or patches of discoloration that exist on the rough surface. Green or brown radiation stains will affect the way in which the actual color of the rough is perceived. Discolored patches on the surface of the rough will also affect the way color is viewed.

Rough diamonds with a glasslike or mirror surface that have a trace of color will tend to concentrate the color towards the points or ribs. The degree in the concentration of color will depend on the overall saturation of color in the body of the rough. Colorless diamonds in this group will retain the same color as observed in the rough.

Frosted or waterworn surfaces will often mask the true color of the rough. If the rough surface is filled with material in which the diamond was extracted, this will further mask the color. Excessive handling with these types of surface will cause dirt to adhere to the surface and will result in a false conclusion of the color.

Grooved or serrated surfaces will distribute the observable body color of the rough in a number of different ways. It can cause an observer that is unfamiliar with this type of surface texture to interpret it quite differently than the actual finished color. **Note:** For the student to overcome some of these deficiencies in rough color grading, it is imperative that a qualified instructor with rough diamond grading experience explain and indicate on a practical level how and when the color is likely to change in certain types of rough.

2. Inclusions. Color can be affected by inclusions in a number of ways. The size, location and number of inclusions may impart varying amount of color to the body of the rough. Dark to black carbon inclusions, particularly if located in small areas throughout the rough, will cause a normally colorless rough to look grayish in color. A feather inclusion that has an orange discoloring will usually cause the bodycolor of a slightly yellow rough to look even more yellow than it is. These and many other areas will need to be considered when color grading rough diamonds.

3. Zoning. Color can be distributed evenly throughout the rough diamond or in layers, spots or bands. If an undesirable color is in spots or layers, the cutter may be able to plan the rough so that it can be removed during the manufacturing process. If only one color layer or zone exists within the diamond, it can influence the entire color of the rough. When color exists in thin long streams, it is referred to as color banding. Color banding can frequently be seen in brown rough diamonds. Depending on the number of bands and intensity of color within the bands and the location of the bands within the rough, the face up saturation of color in the finished diamond will vary considerably. This can be an advantage or it could be detrimental depending on whether the color is desirable or not. A desirable color is one in which the saturation level is deep enough to be considered a fancy color.

4. Size. Color can be affected by the size of the rough diamond. To bring this to an understandable language, let us consider the following.

    a. A given octahedron with a light yellow body color when sawed off center will produce one larger piece of rough and one smaller.

    b. The larger piece can have approximately 70% of the total weight of the rough and the other piece can have approximately 30% of the remaining weight. (Note: A dodecahedron with good spread and shape in the right weight category can be sawed to produce these percentages).

    c. Both sawed pieces when completed processing will yield approximately 50% of their original weight.

    d. The difference in relation to the size of each piece will cause the color to be several shades different.

    e. The larger finished diamond will draw more body color than the smaller piece.

The above case can produce an even greater difference in color if color zoning is present in the larger piece.

The most frequently encountered colors are colorless to varying shades of yellow to various shades of brown. True desirable fancy colors are far less frequently encountered. Borderline colors that may not fall as a fancy color can be pushed into the fancy color category by the type of cut and shape that is used on the rough. Interpretation of surface, inclusions, zoning and size combined together is all-important to accurately access color in rough diamonds. The following photographs will give the student a visual idea of color in rough.

5.1

Photo 5.1 reveals a parcel of rough diamonds ranging from colorless to varying shades of yellow to brown. (See enlarged photo on the front jacket cover)

5.2

86

Photo 5.2 shows a sharp contrast of colors in a rough parcel including those that have a fancy color.

5.3

We can observe in photograph 5.3 shades of yellow to brown to colorless.

5.4

The range of colors seen in photo 5.4 are from colorless to varying shades of yellow. Notice the rough in the center top row, it has a slight external shade of green. This rough will finish in the colorless range.

5.5

This group of rough in photo 5.5 is mixed with two colors. A trace of green with the yellow color being more dominant. Whenever this occurs the finished diamond will have a yellow bodycolor.

5.6

Various shades of yellow and brown are present in the group of rough shown in photo 5.6. The top and bottom two pieces on the left have a shade more of brown than yellow.

5.7

Photo 5.7 displays varying degrees of green pigment on the surface. Rough diamonds of this type will usually finish in the colorless range.

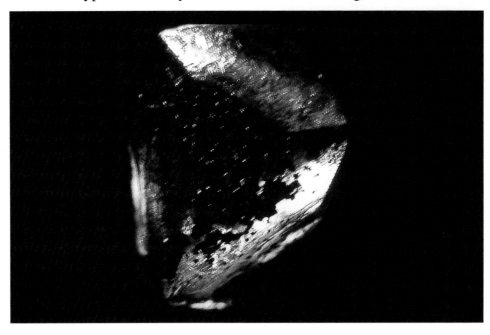

5.8

Photo 5.8 is a close up of an octahedral face revealing how densely radiation stains can cover the surface of the rough.

5.9

Photo 5.9 displays a typical range of yellow colors encountered in rough diamonds.

5.10

We can observe a more saturated range of yellow colors in photo 5.10.

5.11

The dodecahedron in photo 5.11 has a yellow greenish cast. The color will be in the yellow range after cutting and polishing.

5.12

The diamond in photo 5.12 has a deep enough saturation of yellow body color in the rough to classify as a fancy yellow color.

5.13

We can observe in photo 5.13 a range of both yellow and brown colors. These type of colors are frequently encountered in the field among the near gem quality category.

5.14

Photo 5.14 is primarily an assortment of brown, yellow and colorless rough diamonds.

5.15

The parcel of rough seen in photo 5.15 is composed mainly of an assortment of fancy colors. The saturation of color in most of them will easily fall in the fancy color category.

5.16

Large discolored inclusions as shown in photo 5.16 will affect the entire body color of the finished diamond as well as the face up appearance.

5.17

Photo 5.17 displays color banding through one of the faces of this octahedron. This type of color banding is frequently observed in brown rough.

5.18

Photo 5.18 shows color that is concentrated in a wide band within the octahedral rough. If the cutter plans the rough so that the color remains in the pavilion area of the finished diamond, the color can very often fall in the fancy color range.

5.19

The color revealed in photo 5.19 is a brown saturation with a deeper concentration towards the center of the octahedron and lighter towards the outer surface. It is obvious that the finished color will be in the brown color range.

5.20

The narrow concentration of color seen in photo 5.20 may exist close to the surface or may extend deep within the rough. Windows can be polished to determine the depth of color and a decision can later be made as to how to plan the rough.

5.21

Color can sometimes be concentrated from very dark to very light within the rough as seen in photo 5.21

5.22

98

We can observe in photo 5.22 a high concentration of carbon inclusions within the rough. This can often cause the body color to take on a grayish look. When a high amount of fluorescence exists a grayish look can also occur. A combination of the preceding two factors is displayed in this rough.

The following eight photographs are finished fancy colored diamonds.

5.23

A fancy bluish color can be observed in this round brilliant shown in photo 5.23.

5.24

Photo 5.24 is an oval shape with a lime green color.

5.25

A fancy brownish yellow round brilliant diamond is seen in photo 5.25.

5.26

An intense fancy pink color is displayed in photo 5.26

5.27

Photo 5.27 is a fancy yellow brown modified square cut.

5.28

A purplish fancy color can be seen in photo 5.28

5.29

Photo 5.29 is of a pear shape diamond with a fancy yellow orange color.

5.30

We can observe in photo 5.30 a typical fancy brown color. This type of brown is the most commonly encountered among fancy colored diamonds.

5.31

Industrial quality diamonds can be seen in photo 5.31. They can come in a variety of colors and surface textures.

5.32

Photo 5.32 is a group of cube shaped industrial diamonds. Notice the intensity of colors when compared to the colorless cube at the bottom center.

Photo 5.31 and 5.32 was included in this section to give the student a visual idea that the knowledge in the separation of industrials from gem quality is extremely important for correct purchasing in the field. This present work does not include industrial rough grading. However it is included in the practical rough diamond grading program at A.I.D.C. Inc.

5.33

Photo 5.33 is a magnified view of a stressed area in a brown diamond. Diamonds with a brown color are known to have a high amount of stress and strain and will therefore have the typical rainbow inclusions (See chapter 4, page 80 number 6)

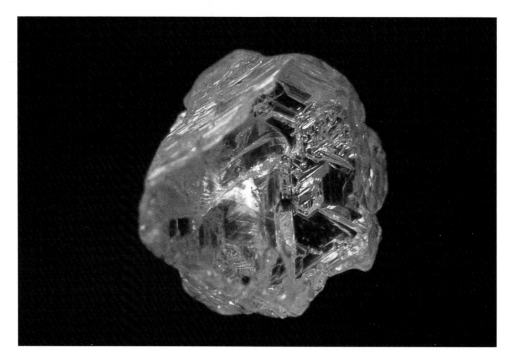

5.34

We can observe another stressed area in photo 5.34. The rough should be examined from several directions in adequate light to detect these types of stress inclusions. (See chapter 4, page 80 number 6)

5.35

A fan shape type inclusion as seen in photo 5.35 indicates severe stress and strain. Notice the partial halo effect. These types of inclusions can easily extend during the manufacturing process. (See chapter 4, page 80, number 6)

CHAPTER SIX
MANUFACTURING ROUGH DIAMONDS

MANUFACTURING ROUGH DIAMONDS
SUMMARY OF FACET PLACEMENT

It would be impossible to thoroughly cover all the aspects of diamond manufacturing in one chapter. We will limit the contents as it applies to the different processes a rough diamond goes through. It will also give the reader an overview of diamond sawing, cutting, polishing, bruting and the application of the rough at different stages.

In the industry there is confusion with the word "cut". It refers in an overall perspective to the facets of a diamond and their relationship to each other and not necessarily the shape of the diamond. A round brilliant as we know has 58 facets, while a fancy shape may have more or less. The word "make" is frequently substituted for the word "cut". One of the objectives of the diamond cutter is to fashion a diamond to permit the maximum amount of light to be reflected through the diamond. It is the cut or make that allows light to reflect from one facet to another and disperse it through the crown to the eye of the observer.

The following diagram (fig.1) reveals that the facets on a completed diamond are of basic geometrical shapes, mostly composed of triangular patterns and straight lines.

These shapes can be both symmetrical or asymmetrical when placed in their correct position on a rough brilliant. They are generally uniform in height and equidistant from side to side.

A description of the 58 facets with respect to their position and size can be described as follows:

A. Table – The largest facet on the diamond, with an octagonal shape. Average industry size of the table is approximately 60% of the average diameter of the finished diamond. The table facet is the most important, it acts as the foundation for all the other facets. (fig.1)

B. Upper girdle facets or top halves – There are sixteen top halves that reach from the girdle toward the table to a height of approximately 55% to 65%. General gemological literature teaches that the height is 50%; among diamond manufactures these facets are fashioned 5% to 15% higher. With the star facets, they form the outline of a kite shape. Their angle is approximately three degrees steeper than the crown mains. Upper girdle facets are located in a pair, side by side. The dividing line between the two is referred to as the crown rib. (fig. 1)

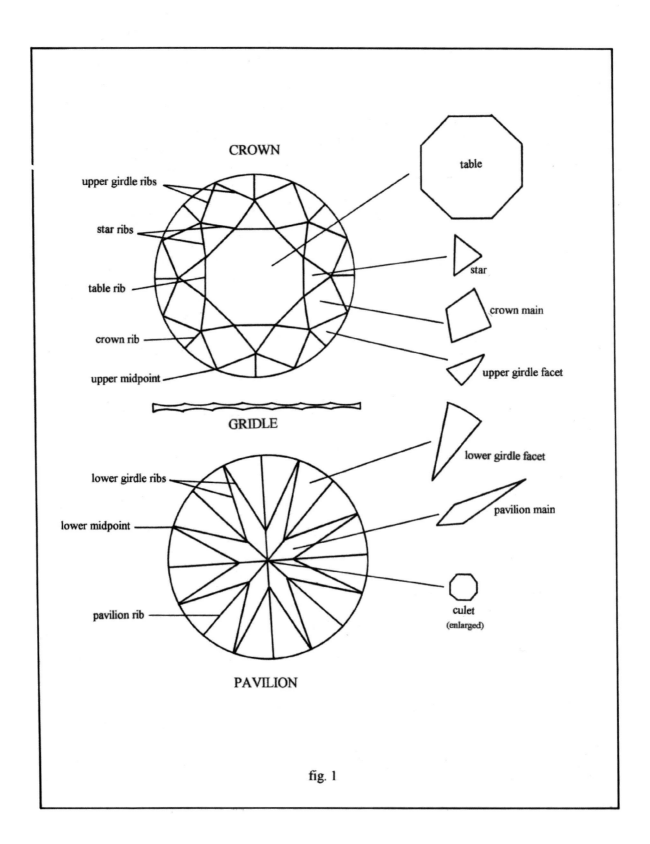

fig. 1

110

C. Stars – There are eight star facets, which are triangular in shape. They reach the midpoint on either side of the crown mains and travel down towards the upper girdle facets. The eight stars form an octagonal shape at the table edge. Their angle is approximately four to five degrees shallower than the crown mains. (fig.1)

D. Crown Mains – There are eight crown mains, each having four sides of which two are shaped by the stars and the other two are shaped by the upper girdle facets. Their final look is a kite shape pattern. Among gemologist they are referred to as bezel facets or crown mains. (fig. 1)

E. Girdle – This is the outer circumference of the diamond where the crown and pavilion is separated by a fine narrow plane. The girdle is shaped by both the crown and pavilion mains along with the upper and lower girdle facets. Depending on the diamond cutter's ability to control the depth of the upper and lower girdle facets, the girdle diameter will be relatively the same thickness as it travels around the diamond. Cutting the crown and pavilion mains will often determine the final thickness of the girdle. The girdle is sometimes faceted to obtain a better finish to the overall cut. The technique of faceting the girdle is where the diamond cutter places small parallel facets around the entire surface of the girdle. (fig. 1)

F. Pavilion mains – There are eight pavilion mains which run from the girdle to form an exact point situated at the center of the pavilion. Their final shape is dictated by the lower girdle facets that shape them to a fine point at the girdle. (fig.1)

G. Lower girdle facets – The sixteen lower girdle facets travel from the girdle to approximately 85% in height towards the culet and 50% across the girdle of the pavilion main. The percentage height of these facets will vary slightly from one cutter to the other. The angle of the lower girdle facets are approximately one to two degrees steeper than the pavilion mains. Just like the upper girdle facets, the lower girdle facets are located in pairs, side by side. The dividing line between the two are referred to as the pavilion rib. (fig. 1)

H. Culet – There is only one culet which is situated at the apex where the eight pavilion mains meet. A miniature facet is cut here which should have the exact shape as the table. The culet facet is cut primarily to avoid chipping or damage to the point created by the pavilion mains. (fig. 1) (At what stage should the culet be cut and polished?) This area will be discussed under the cutting and polishing section of this chapter.

For these 58 facets to arrive to their final shape, a foundation of initial facets are usually laid out on which the diamond cutter builds. This foundation will be examined in detail and the order in which they are placed at a later point.

TERMINOLOGY CLARIFICATION.

For us to proceed with a clear understanding of the manufacturing process we will need to clarify certain terminology that is used in this chapter, and, at the same time, point out some of their duplicate usage. For simplicity we will select one meaning for each word. Following is a list of words that will need to be understood.

1. Cutting – This is the process of grinding a facet on the lap or wheel. The surface of the facet has fine parallel lines that are produced by the course surface of the lap. These lines are referred to as cutting lines. The word "cutting" can also be used to mean both the cutting and polishing process.

2. Polishing – The process of polishing is a back and forth action that is done on the lap to remove the cutting lines. The facet, when properly polished, is perfectly flat without any blemish. (NOTE-The word cutting and polishing can be used in conjunction with each other to signify the entire process of a completed facet or all the facets of a diamond.)

3. Smoothing – This word has the same meaning as polishing.

4. Roughing out – The process of cutting large mains or facets to shape a diamond. It allows the diamond cutter to determine the final placement of the crown and pavilion mains. None of these preliminary mains are polished until final decisions are made with regard to the final layout of the diamond.

5. Blocking – This is when a diamond cutter cuts and polishes eight crown mains, one table, eight pavilion mains, and one culet. The diamond is then referred to as a, "blocked diamond or a single cut".

6. In-Cross – This is the process of cutting and /or polishing four crown and pavilion mains opposite to each other, one table, and one culet.

7. Bruting or girdling – Both words have the same meaning. It is the process of shaping the diamond to a round or fancy shape outline. It is usually done by rotating the diamond around its center axis and using another diamond in a fixed position to create the desired outline.

8. Mains – Refers to the first eight facets on the crown and the first eight on the pavilion.

9. Grain – This is usually referred to as the cutting, polishing, and sawing planes of a diamond. Utilizing the grain perpendicular to the direction it travels will allow ease of cutting, polishing, and sawing.

10. Brillianteer – The cutting and polishing process of the upper girdle facets (16), star facets (8), and lower girdle facets (16). A total of 40 facets. This is a follow-through process after the diamond has been blocked.

11. Faceted girdle – Refers to the small parallel facets placed around the circumference of the girdle.

THE FOUR STEPS OF MANUFACTURING A ROUGH DIAMOND.

There are basically four steps in manufacturing a rough diamond. In each of the following four steps, there may be one or more subdivisions.

1. Studying the rough diamond.
   A. Marking

2. Dividing the rough diamond (sawing and cleaving)
   A. Sawing
   B. Cleaving

3. Girdling or bruting the rough diamond.

4. Cutting and polishing the rough diamond
   A. Roughing out
   B. Blocking
   C. Brillianteering

1. STUDYING THE ROUGH DIAMOND.

Before a diamond cutter attempts to do anything, an intensive study of the diamond is required, usually through a loupe (with 10x magnification) or a microscope. A study of the inclusions within the diamond is made to determine which can be removed during the cutting, polishing, and bruting process. In the case of a rough octahedron, the feasibility of aligning any inclusion along the sawing plane will also be determined.

During this study, the direction of the grain and the way it is situated in the rough diamond will have to be examined. The diamond cutter will decide the angle and shape that will retain as much of the original weight as possible. During this examination, the diamond cutter has to consider the crystal classification, whether the diamond has a good shape (octahedral crystal), cleavage (triangular shape, cleaved from an octahedral face), macle (twinned triangular rough), or a flat (thin triangular or irregular rough). The shape of the rough will determine how the diamond will be cut and polished and what form it will become when cut. The final weight and clarity play a major role in deciding the final outcome. (For crystal structure, shape and classification refer to chapter two.)

6.1

A. Marking

Rough diamonds, other than octahedrons, are carefully marked with India or indelible ink to show where the table will fall, resulting in a follow through process of crown and pavilion placement. Octahedrons and dodecahedrons are marked to indicate their sawing planes. (photo 6.1) The surface of this division usually becomes the table. This marking actually directs the entire cutting and polishing operation. A well-shaped octahedron can be fashioned into two round brilliant cuts of the same size or one smaller

114

and the other larger. (fig. 2) An elongated octahedron may be cut into an oval, marquise, or emerald cut diamond.

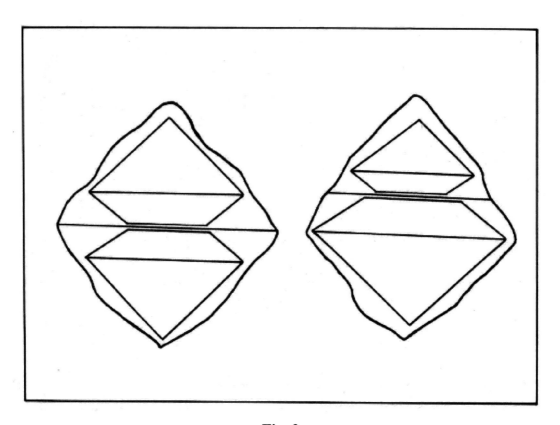

Fig. 2

6.2

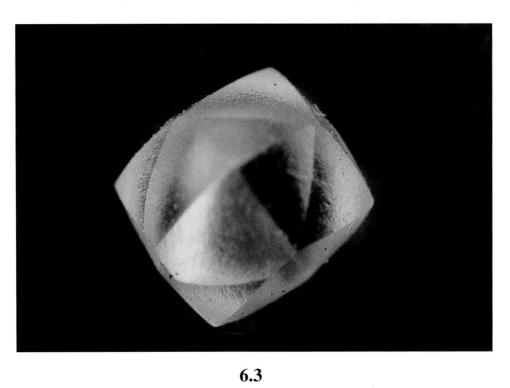

6.3

116

2. DIVIDING THE ROUGH DIAMOND (CLEAVING AND SAWING)

The most common shape a diamond crystal takes is an octahedron (photo 6.2) and dodecahedron (modified octahedron). (photo 6.3) Although a diamond is the hardest of all natural substances, it has hard and soft directions; this is usually referred to as the "grain". The diamond cutter relates all his work to what is called the grain of the diamond; thus, he polishes, cuts, and saws perpendicular to the grain. This is defined as the softest direction. The grain is represented by fine parallel lines forming a triangle seen on most octahedral faces. When the grain is not seen on the surface, the shape of the diamond will indicate its pattern. The grain exist inside the diamond and is related to the crystal axis and structure. An experienced diamond cutter can figure the entire grain structure of a finished diamond based only on the polishing lines of a few facets.

6.4

A. Sawing

This is the modern method of obtaining two or more diamonds from a single rough. Diamonds are sawed on a sawing machine with a very thin phosphor-bronze disc which is between 3 to 4 inches in diameter and a thickness between 0.06mm to 0.15mm. A driving belt turns the sawing blade at speeds from 8,500 to 12,500 revolutions per minute, according to the needs of the sawer. The edge of the blade is coated with a paste of olive oil and diamond dust (since only a diamond can cut another diamond). The diamond to be sawed

117

is cemented into a female center and held by another. The diamond is placed over the blade and is fed by gravity. As the diamond saws, the arm of the sawing machine is gradually lowered. It takes anywhere from thirty minutes to several hours to saw through a one carat rough diamond. (photo 6.4) The sawer saws in a non-cleaving direction. There are two normal directions of sawing, one in the cube direction and the other in the dodecahedral. The sawer calls this four point sawing and two point sawing. It is almost impossible to saw diamonds in another direction, even if only a few degrees different.

6.5

B. Cleaving

Cleaving is the original method that was used to separate or divide a diamond. A common misconception among laymen is the belief that cutting is cleaving and that the faceting and shaping is like a chipping and sculpting operation. The process of cleaving is done simply by setting the diamond in a cemented dop or holder and using another diamond to create a v-shape groove in line with the desired plane of separation. A square edged knife is inserted into the groove and is tapped sharply with a mallet. It is absolutely imperative that the groove started, is in a precise cleaving direction, any other direction may cause the diamond to shatter. Cleaving can only be done parallel to an octahedral plane or face (photo 6.5). Cleaving is considered the most dramatic of all the steps in

118

diamond manufacturing because the whole future of the diamond rests on that one tap of the mallet. Today this method is mainly used for very large irregular shapes and small included rough diamonds. Sawing has almost completely replaced cleaving.

6.6

3. BRUTING OR GIRDLING THE ROUGH DIAMOND.

The next step requires a lathe type machine which rotates at a speed of 800 to 1,400 revolutions per minute. The diamond to be bruted is cemented on a holder which is placed on a revolving shaft. Another diamond is selected as the cutting tool tip, which is cemented to a similar holder at the end of a stick about two feet long. The girdler, or better known as the bruter, holds the stick under his arm and applies the diamond at the end of it to the diamond which is rotated in the lathe. There is a U-rest for the stick at the front of the lathe and also a pan to receive the diamond dust. It is obvious that this process is a forcing one because the grain is ignored. Thus, the bruter makes the girdle (largest circumference) of the diamond in the same plane as the table (largest facet). (photo 6.6).

Diamonds finished in the oval, marquise, and pear shapes usually go through the same steps, but by a slightly different process. In the larger fancy shapes, the girdle is usually faceted. Emerald-cut diamonds have their gridle formed during the cutting and polishing operation.

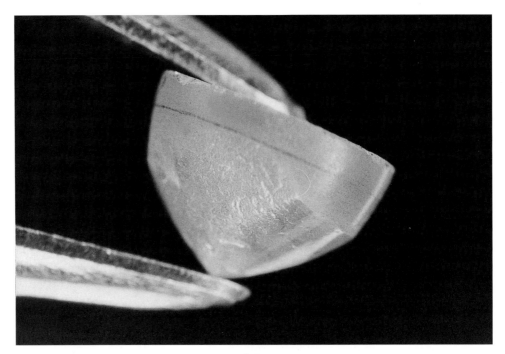

6.7

6.8

After the diamond has been bruted and sufficient girdle thickness is made to accommodate the desired crown height percentage, the diamond is marked with a line around the girdle to give the diamond cutter a guide as to where the crown and pavilion girdle plane will fall. (photo 6.7) This procedure is accomplished on an instrument called a girdle marker. The girdle marker is a simple device that raises or lowers a circular copper blade that has a tapered edge. After the desired crown height adjustment is made the diamond is turned in a circular motion just touching the blade against the frosted girdle. (photo 6.8) This will mark a sharp narrow line for the diamond cutter. The line is later removed by acid after the diamond is completed.

Before we consider the actual process of cutting and polishing, we need to examine briefly the equipment for cutting and polishing and the specific grain structure that the diamond cutter encounters.

6.9

121

6.10

The diamond cutting unit consists of a one horse power motor that is attached to a horizontal grinding wheel which revolves approximately 2,400 to 3,500 revolutions per minute. (photo 6.9) The wheel or lap is made of cast iron, impregnated with oil and diamond dust. The abrasive action of the diamond powder tears at the surface of the diamond which creates a cutting action. A back and forth movement on a specially prepared area on the wheel creates a highly polished surface. (photo 6.10).

6.11

6.12

The diamond is held in a claw like holder known as a dop which is attached to an arm (known as a tang) that the diamond cutter uses to make the necessary adjustment

123

during the cutting and polishing of each facet. (See photo 6.11 and 6.12) The surface of the wheel or lap is divided into three areas:

    A.   The testing ring, which is used to find the correct starting point of a facet through judgment and by trial and error.

    B.   The running or cutting ring, on which the facet is ground to size.

    C.   The polishing ring is for polishing the facet to a perfect flat surface, by removing the grooves and running lines caused by grinding.

6.13

3 point grain - Table facet is situated on an octahedral face. (photo 6.13)

2 point grain - Table facet is situated on an octahedral rib. (photo 6.13)

4 point grain - Table facet is situated over an octahedral point. (photo 6.13)

The diamond cutter has to decide upon a plan of action before he starts the exacting work of grinding and polishing.   This will first depend upon the relation of the crystal structure to the final brilliant cut. To put it another way, how the diamond is cut will depend upon whether it is a four point, three point, or two point diamond. These terms are explained in relation to structure in the above photo. (photo 6.13)

A.   To the diamond cutter, a four point is one in which the table originally had four corners or the table facet is oriented to the cube plane. It may be an irregular diamond (known as a whole stone) or more commonly part of a sawed octahedron. The separation plane of the sawed octahedron is automatically oriented to the four-point grain. It also indicates the cutting and polishing direction of the four point grain.

B.   A three point diamond has a table, which was originally an octahedral face with three corners. It may be an irregular diamond, a macle, or a cleaved diamond.

C.   A two point diamond has the table in a rhombic dodecahedral direction, that is, it is along one of the straight edges or ribs of an octahedral crystal, and, therefore, has only two corners. This can also form in nature as an irregular shape.

To sum it up, taking the most common of the rough diamonds as an example, the octahedron has eight faces, twelve ribs and six points. The ribs or ridges are called two point, the triangular faces three point, and the four corners forming a cube four point. The significance of this is that in a given octahedron one of its grains will be used as the main facet known as the table. This ultimately decides the cutting and polishing positions of each facet.

(a)   Four point – As discussed previously, a four point grain is usually found on an octahedron or modified octahedron. The table is usually placed on any point of the octahedron.

(b)   Three point – This type of grain structure is found on the face of an octahedron, normally an irregular diamond, such as a macle (flat triangular shape) or a cleaved rough.

(c)   Two point – To obtain a two point grain, the table will have to be placed on the rib of a diamond. This edge can be either sharp and straight or in most cases curved and modified. This type of grain structure is found in irregular shaped diamonds, resulting in a thicker rough diamond as compared to a flat or macle.

What is meant by cutting on grain? It is orienting the diamond to a position anywhere in a 360 degrees circle and placing the diamond on the wheel or lap so that it cuts perpendicular to the specific grain of that facet. This quality in a diamond distinguishes it from all other gemstones. To achieve the optimum polish the facet must be cut and polished perpendicular to the grain. A facet that is forced, lacks reflective luster, and blurs the refractive quality inherent in a diamond.

4. CUTTING AND POLISHING THE ROUGH DIAMOND.

The cutting and polishing process is considered the final step in manufacturing a diamond. This process is subdivided into three stages.

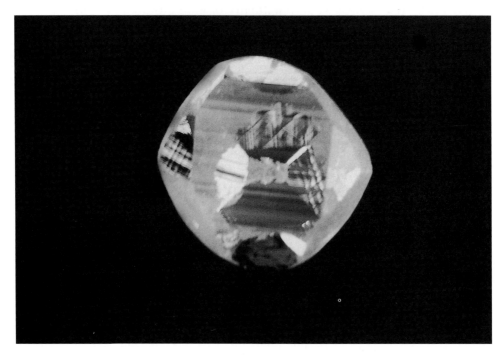

6.14

A. Roughing out

Roughing out is the cutting process in which material is preliminarily removed from the diamond to establish the correct orientation. The diamond is shaped through the placement of table, crown, and pavilion facets. The facet angles are cut steeper to allow room for adjustment prior to the final cutting and polishing. This initial process provides the diamond cutter the opportunity to tilt the table, rearrange the entire diamond for better weight retention or chase after inclusions that can possibly be removed. The roughing out process is used primarily for rough diamonds other than octahedrons. (whole diamonds) (photo 6.14)

6.15

6.16

6.17

B. Blocking

The table which is the largest facet of the diamond, is usually the surface formed when the diamond is sawed or cleaved. The girdle is formed with its side perpendicular to the table. The diamond cutter, if seeking ideal proportions, grinds and polishes a facet between the table and girdle at an angle of 34.50° to the plane of the girdle. (photo 6.15) He now grinds a second facet directly opposite the first. Next, he grinds two more facets, on either side, exactly right angles to the first two. These are called the crown mains. (photo 6.16) The diamond is then turned over and four corresponding pavilion mains are placed below the girdle, each on 40.75° to the girdle plane. (photo 6.17) The diamond is now in -cross.

6.18

6.19

The first two mains that are cut and polished on the pavilion, which are opposite to each other create a ridge where they meet. A straight narrow facet is cut and polished on this ridge. (photo 6.18) When the other two pavilion mains are made to the correct angle and depth in the girdle, they close the long narrow facet to a perfect square. This creates the initial outline for a culet. (photo. 6.19) We can clearly see that the culet is made during the blocking process and is not the last facet to be made as commonly believed. (NOTE: In the general manufacturing industry, a culet is normally placed on diamonds that are 0.50ct. and larger. Smaller diamonds are manufactured without a culet and are usually brought to a sharp point.)

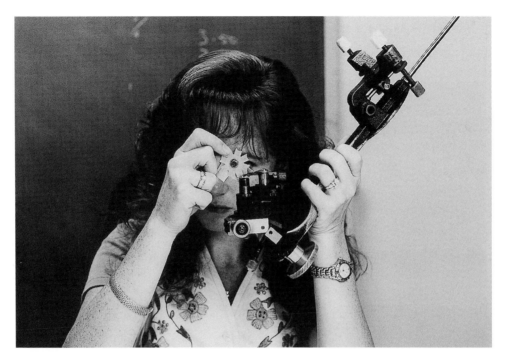

6.20

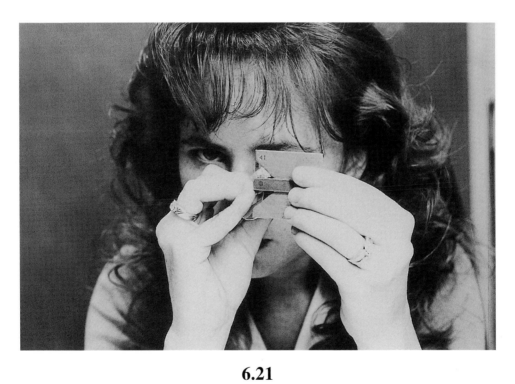

6.21

To arrive at the angle for the crown and pavilion, an angle gauge is affixed to the side of the tang and is set to keep the angles consistent. A hand gauge called a star gauge can also be used for the crown angles (photo 6.20) or a butterfly gauge for the pavilion. (photo 6.21)

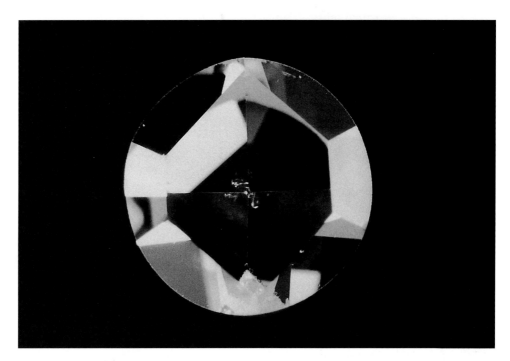

6.22

6.23

In the second stage of blocking, four more crown mains are placed above the girdle. Two mains are first placed opposite to each other. (photo 6.22) Each is exactly between two of the first four facets. There are four more pavilion mains that are placed, which correspond to the second four mains on the crown. (photo 6.23) The point at which all eight pavilion mains meet forms a miniature octagonal shape, which can now be referred to as the culet.

The entire process has to be checked repeatedly to see that not too much is being ground away on any one facet. With the grinding and polishing of these surfaces, it is very important that the correct angles are maintained because the entire symmetry and fire of the final gem depend upon the accuracy with which these facets are placed.

6.24

At this point, the diamond looks like the familiar round brilliant. It has 18 facets, of which there are 8 crown mains, the table above the girdle and 8 pavilion mains meeting at the culet below the girdle. The table, if not already polished, should be polished at this time. For most diamonds that are less than 0.02 carat in weight, this can be the end of the line. Such diamonds with only 18 facets are called single cuts. On larger diamonds, this is referred to as a blocked diamond. (photo 6.24)

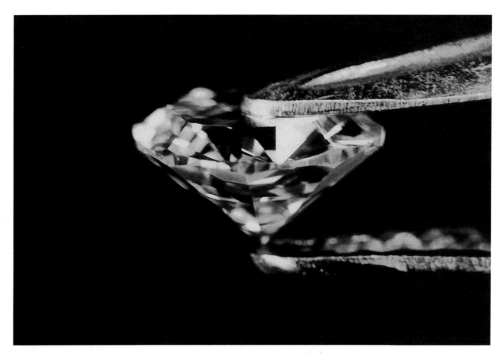

6.25

At this point the girdle of the diamond can be faceted (photo 6.25). This gives the diamond a more complete finish and allows additional light to enter the diamond. Fine quality finished diamonds that are expected to have a grading report usually have a faceted girdle. If the girdle is faceted after the brillianteering process, most of the upper and lower girdle facets will have to be re-closed at their midpoint.

6.26

6.27

135

6.28

C. Brillianteering

This is the last stage where the diamond cutter achieves the final beauty of a diamond. Sixteen facets are cut and polished above the girdle. These are known as the upper girdle facets or top halves. (photo 6.26). Below the girdle, sixteen additional facets are cut, they are similar to the top halves, but are much longer. These are known as the lower girdle facets or bottom halves. (photo 6.27) Finally, eight star facets are cut where the crown mains meet the table. (photo 6.28)   This comprises a total of 40 facets in brillianteering.

6.29

A great deal of skill and judgment is needed to brillianteer because the facets cut quickly and need to be inspected every few seconds to make sure that the angle and size are correct. A total of 58 facets have been cut and polished, the diamond is now known as a full cut. (photo 6.29) (Note: the 58 facets does not include the facets placed around the girdle)

Diamond cutting is a long exacting process since cutters must stop and check the accuracy of their work continuously. The finished diamond is a gem of beauty, exactly proportioned, returning light in a dazzling array of brilliance.

TECHNOLOGY IN DIAMOND MANUFACTURING

To continue our insight into the diamond manufacturing process, this chapter would not be complete without a look at the future of diamond technology along with discussing some misconceptions that are already prevalent in the industry. Because of the diamond's hardness, it is unique in this respect. Certain processes during manufacturing can be automated, but each diamond has to be considered independently. We will briefly examine each manufacturing process for its present and future potential.

137

A. Sawing

This process has been the most resistant to change. The basic sawing machine has remained unaltered for generations. Only recently have simple devices been attached to the sawing machine to assist in this operation. One device is a pressure sensitive pad that monitors the rate of feed at which the diamond saws. This results in sawing the diamond in a minimum time period.

The laser has played an important role in the separation and outline shaping of the rough diamond. Most diamonds that cannot be sawed by the conventional method, because of natts (knots) or crossgraining, are lasered. Lasering does not need to take into consideration grain direction. Its main drawback is the damage that may occur to a diamond due to the intense heat that occurs while lasering. The future hold tremendous advantages and versatility using a cold laser process. It is the author's opinion that it will eventually be possible to effectively use a cold laser process to shape as well as pre-form a rough diamond, thereby reducing the cutting and polishing time considerably.

B. Bruting

This process has been traditionally accomplished by bruting a single diamond at a time. One skilled operator is needed to operate one machine. Bruting machines are now available that have the capability of bruting two round gem quality diamonds simultaneously. An operator can run six or more machines at the same time. The traditional gluing process for mounting diamonds is still used. One of the side benefit to the diamond manufacturing industry as a result of this new type of bruting machine is the development of a centering system. After the diamond is glued on the bruting dop, and, before it is placed on the bruting machine, it is centered to obtain the maximum spread from the rough. It is then placed on the machine and bruted to completion without any further adjustment. Bruting fancy shapes is still done by the traditional method. The future has excellent possibilities of automating the process of fancy diamond bruting combined with new methods of mounting and unmounting the diamond.

C. Cutting and Polishing

The greatest strides in new technology has been made in this area. Automatic production type cutting and polishing is done on rough diamonds with each unit handling one diamond. The traditional cutting bench is still employed with two to four automated units on each cutting bench. The units are capable of cutting and polishing approximately forty-eight of the fifty-eight facets on a round brilliant. If a problem is encountered during processing, the unit will skip that particular facet and go on to the next. The skipped facets as well as the facets the unit is not capable of completing is done by the traditional process. Advancement in this area of technology is ongoing and will hold many surprises in the near future. The idea of multiple faceting heads on one unit is just a matter of time, as well as, having the capability of cutting and polishing all fifty-eight facets.

We will now examine some misconceptions that exist in the diamond industry and especially the jewelry industry with regard to the mode of processing.

The term, "machine cut" or laser cut", is frequently quoted by many in the trade. Do not be misled by these or any other similar terminology. The words, "machine cut", is used to suggest that a diamond cut by a machine will be better or more precisely cut and polished than traditional cutting and polishing methods.

First, let us sort fact from fantasy. The quality of the cut on a diamond can be good or poor, regardless of whether the facets were placed by a machine or the traditional methods. Quality of cut is dependent on the skill of the diamond cutter or the skill of the operator of an automated machine, as well as, the capabilities of that machine. Presently, there exist machines that can cut and polish up to 83% of a round brilliant. The remaining facets are cut and polished by traditional methods. Fine quality rough diamonds, especially in larger sizes, are all polished by traditional methods. However, the repetitive standard that can be achieved by an automated process does not warrant constant supervision for the highest in cut and polish. It is, therefore, reserved for average and lower quality diamonds. Cutting and polishing fancy shapes by automation is still an accomplishment to be explored by future technology.

Laser cutting does not mean that diamonds are cut and polished by lasers. It is the process of dividing diamonds, similar to sawing or shaping the outline of a diamond. Lasers are used for shaping outlines such as stars, alphabet letters, and most type of free form shapes, since the grain of the diamond does not need to be addressed. The surface produced by lasers have fine parallel lines similar to those found in the sawing process. Mainly better quality diamonds, preferably without stress or major feathers, are used for lasering. The reason for this is because the heat created during laser shaping can sometimes be detrimental to the diamond. After the diamond is lasered, it still has to go through the cutting and polishing process. Lasers have extremely limited use in diamond recutting and repairing. Lasers are often used to turn a black inclusion to white. The idea behind this is that a diamond with a white appearing inclusion is more saleable than one with a black appearance. The method used is to drill a fine hole perpendicular to the table plane, soak the diamond in acid to bleach the inclusion, and fill the top section of the hole with epoxy. Lasers and other technology will continue to play a valuable role in the diamond manufacturing process.

PRACTICAL APPLICATION IN MANUFACTURING ROUGH DIAMONDS

The following are specific areas of information in the manufacturing process that the rough buyer will need to be aware of during the analysis of single large pieces of rough. By no means is it a comprehensive coverage, however the areas covered are critical for a better understanding of the rough. These and many additional areas are covered in the practical rough diamond grading program at A.I.D.C. Inc.

A. General

6.30

We can observe in photo 6.30 a rough octahedron marked slightly above the middle. This is referred to as topping in which one larger and one smaller piece will result when completed. (compare photo 6.1, marked for halving) Marking the diamond is one of the most critical decisions in manufacturing the rough, since this will decide the outcome of the finished diamond with regard to size and clarity.

6.31

Photo 6.31 is an aerial view at the point in which the sawer stopped just short of exiting the rough along the sawing plane. Notice the lip remaining at the point of the octahedron. Instead of sawing to completion the sawer saves time by backing the blade out of the sawing plane and gently snapping the rough. This is a normal sawing technique, which will not harm the rough diamond.

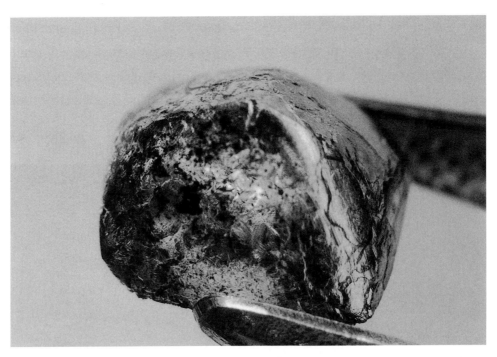

6.32

The surface of the sawed rough seen in photo 6.32 is covered with green radiation stains. It is extremely difficult to locate any internal inclusions with this type of surface. (see also photo 6.33)

6.33

142

Photo 6.33 is an internal view of the sawed rough previously shown in photo 6.32. Examining the diamond along the sawed plane under high magnification, we can observe three inclusions. It would have been impossible to detect these small inclusions them through this particular type of surface on the rough.

6.34

In photo 6.34 we see a polished window on the surface of the sawed rough. The window was opened before sawing to determine the best possible way to orient the rough. It is always a good idea to open windows whenever the rough surface does not allow visibility within.

6.35

The rough in photo 6.35 has a frosted surface, however we can clearly see several carbon inclusion on the inside.

6.36

Photo 6.36 is an aerial view of the rough photographed in photo 6.35. It was sawed with the idea of retaining all the inclusions on one side (see photo 6.37)

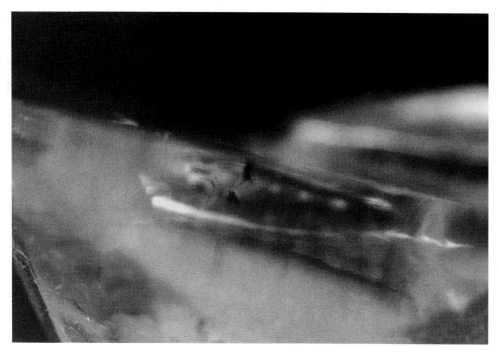

6.37

Photo 6.37 is a side view of one of the sawed pieces from photo 6.36, clearly showing the carbon inclusions just under the table plane. The diamond cutter now has the option of either leaving the inclusions under the table or removing it by lowering the table plane, resulting in a smaller but less included diamond.

B. Sawing twinned (knotted) rough

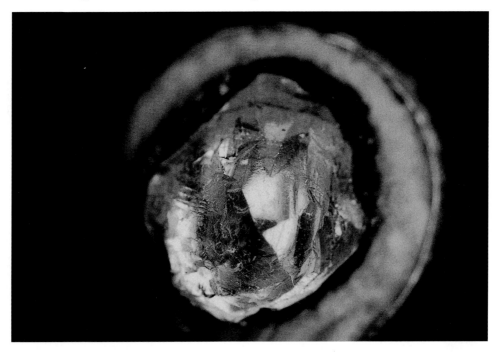

6.38

Photo 6.38 is an aerial view of a twinned diamond mounted in a sawing pot for sawing. (see also photo 6.39 & 6.40)

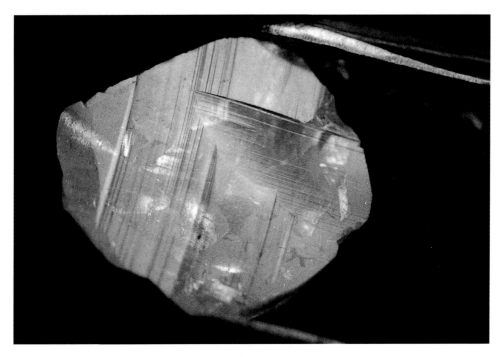

6.39

Many times the sawer has to saw from several directions along the same plane when a twinned or knotted area is encountered internally. Photo 6.39 is the sawed plane of the same rough shown in photo 6.38. Notice the saw lines that run in different directions.

6.40

Photo 6.40 is a side view of the sawing plane of another twinned rough. We can observe the curved direction of the blade upon encountering the knot. To level the table plane an additional 1% of the rough weight will be lost.

Following is a step by step photo documentation of what can go wrong when sawing a knotted diamond. (photo 6.41 to 6.47) The most dangerous aspect during the manufacturing process is the sawing. The simple fact that a high speed flexible metal blade is traveling through the body of a diamond does pose a certain danger to the rough, especially when a knot, twin line or inclusion is encountered.

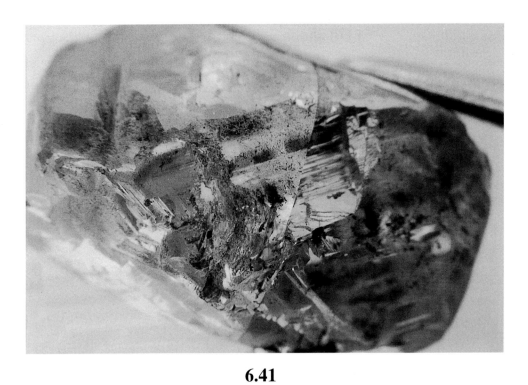

6.41

The rough in photo 6.41 with the attached broken piece weighs 13.85cts.

6.42

Photo 6.42 is a view of the smaller broken piece that is lifted away from the main rough. The smaller piece weighs 4.98cts.

6.43

In photo 6.43, we can see the angle of the break, which exist in a cleavage direction from the main body of the rough. This larger remaining piece now weighs 8.45cts. We can also view a projected area above the saw plane in which the blade met at the knotted junction. The blade was put through the diamond from three directions meeting at the knotted projected area before breaking.

6.44

Photo 6.44 reveals both the cleaved surface of the 4.98ct piece and the three sawing directions on the surface of the saw plane.

6.45

An attempt was made to saw the remaining portion from the 8.45ct rough. Photo 6.45 reveals the different sawing directions that converged towards the knotted area.

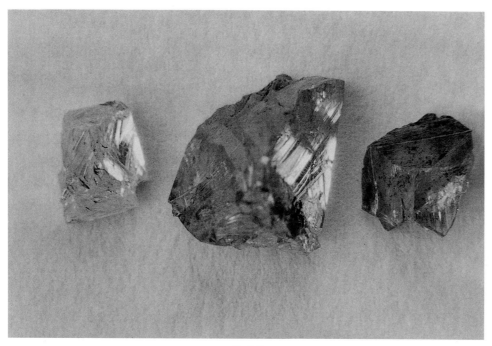

6.46

Photo 6.46 is the result of what occurred when the rough broke the second time. It shattered the upper remaining portion in three pieces.

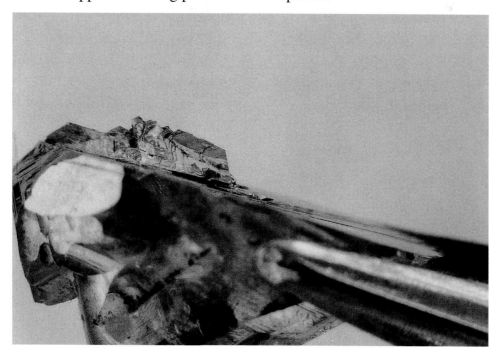

6.47

The larger portion of the rough is shown from a side view in photo 6.47. The protruded area along the saw plane is what remains of the knotted area. This protruding area will later be cut on the cutting lap to create a level surface.

C. Lasering

When a rough has multiple or single twinning which poses a problem for normal sawing, it is usually considered for lasering. The following photos are of rough diamonds that have been lasered.

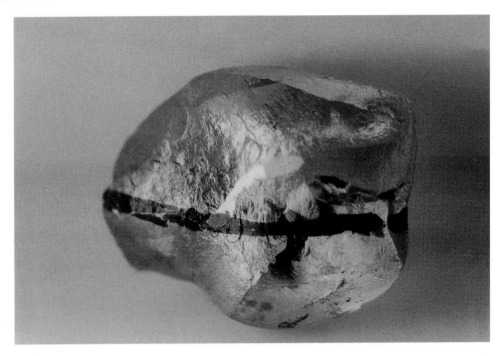

6.48

In photo 6.48 we can observe a 2.24ct whole rough twinned diamond marked for lasering.

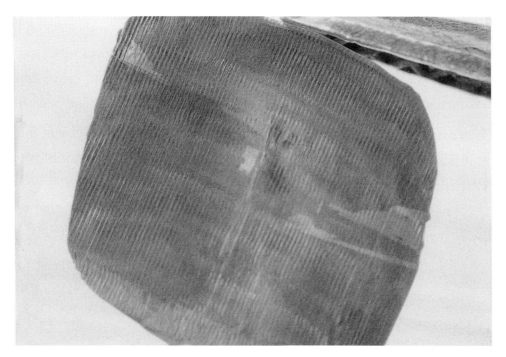

6.49

Photo 6.49 is a normal lasered surface. The fine parallel lines along the laser plane are similar to saw lines. The surface color can range from light gray, dark gray to almost black. The heat produced by the laser causes the grayish surface color.

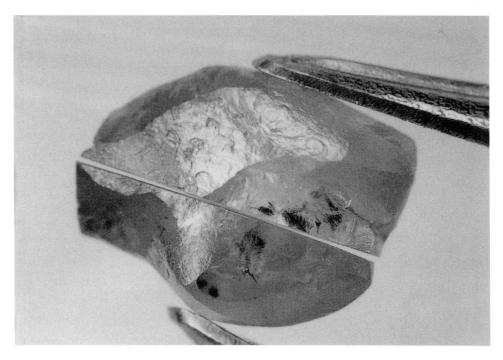

6.50

A lasered 2.24ct rough diamond is shown in photo 6.50. (see also the same rough marked in photo 6.48) We can observe that the top and bottom pieces touch each other in the middle with a space on either side. The reason for this is that the diamond was lasered from each side towards the center. A laser makes a wedge shape cut rather than a straight parallel cut. This of course results in a greater weight loss as compared to sawing. The weight loss on this 2.24ct. lasered rough was 7.58% as opposed to 2% with standard sawing. Lasering does not need to take into account grain direction.

6.51

Photo 6.51 shows the grayish lasered surface of the larger piece displayed in photo 6.50. We can also see the carbon inclusions under the surface that can also be observed from a side view shown in photo 6.50.

D.   Internal Inclusions.

Rough diamonds that are sawn in a plane that intersect inclusions within the body of the rough will normally be considered for partial or complete removal during the cutting and polishing process. In the following photographs we will consider these possibilities.

6.52

Photo 6.52 is a sawed piece weighing 2.43cts. There are both single and groups of carbon inclusions that are visible through the saw plane. (see also photo 6.53)

6.53

In photo 6.53 we can examine a magnified view of the inclusions shown in photo 6.52. The group of inclusions on the right are closer to the table surface while the fuzzy appearance of the inclusions on the left are deeper.

6.54

Examining the same rough shown in photo 6.53, we can just observe in photo 6.54 some of the inclusions through the rough octahedral surface.

6.55

Photo 6.55 reveals a 2.43ct rough diamond that is partially manufactured. We can clearly see inclusions located at various depths through a pavilion facet.

6.56

We can see in photo 6.56 the blocked (8mains on the crown and 8 mains on the pavilion) 2.43ct rough. The two smaller inclusions that was observed in photo 6.55 through the pavilion were located close to the table facet. The table was enlarged to remove 90% of these inclusions.

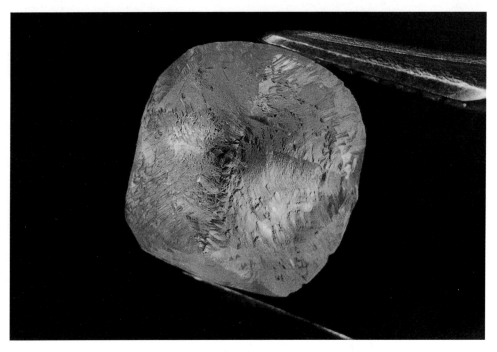

6.57

Photo 6.57 is an aerial view of a sawed rough, looking through the sawed plane. The rough surface on the outside has a frosted texture. We can observe at 12 o' clock a small feather inclusion. (see also photo 6.58)

6.58

Photo 6.58 is a magnified view of the feather inclusions seen in photo 6.57. During the manufacturing process the table facet can be made larger to remove the inclusion.

E. Fancy Shapes

Rough diamonds that lend themselves to fancy shapes are usually fashioned from one single piece of rough. The normal exception is when an octahedron or dodecahedron is oriented and sawed to produce two elongated rectangular shapes. In these cases the rectangular shapes are manufactured into, step cut emeralds, radiant, barion or princess cuts. Following are rough shapes that lend themselves to different fancy cuts.

6.59

This type of rough shape that is shown in photo 6.59 can be manufactured into a triangular cut, possibly a pear shape or a round brilliant with a little additional weight loss.

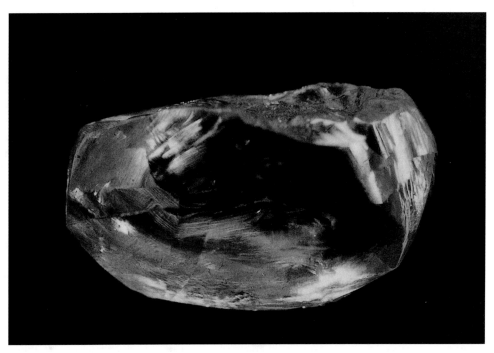

6.60

160

Photo 6.60 shows a rough with an elongated form that can be cut into an oval or marquise shape.

6.61

The outline of the rough in photo 6.61 is ideally suited to be manufactured into an oval shape.

6.62

The rough shape in photo 6.62 can be cut into a step cut emerald, radiant or barion cut.

6.63

The macle in photo 6.63 has three straight sides, its best option for maximum weight retention would be a triangular cut.

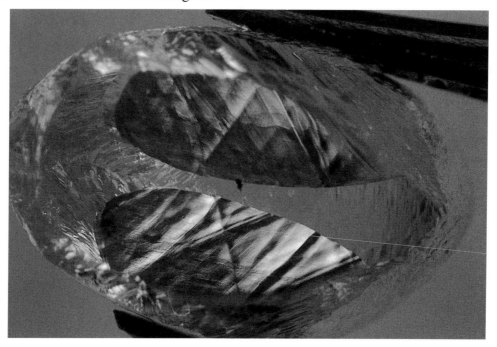

6.64

Photo 6.64 is an ideal shape 3.62ct rough that can be manufactured into a marquise cut. Notice the three facets that are already cut, the table and two pavilion facets. We can observe a carbon inclusion in the center of the rough under the table. (see also photo 6.65)

6.65

Photo 6.65 is the completed marquise that was cut from the 3.62ct rough as shown in photo 6.64. We can see the carbon inclusion still remaining in the finished diamond. The marquise finished weight was 1.45ct.

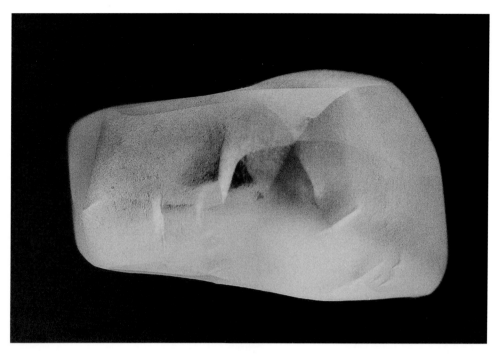

6.66

Shown in photo 6.66 is a rectangular shape rough. It is naturally suited for a step cut emerald shape. (see also photo 6.67).

6.67

Photo 6.67 is the manufactured rectangular shape rough that was seen in photo 6.66.

CHAPTER SEVEN

VALUING ROUGH DIAMONDS

VALUING ROUGH DIMAONDS

1. GENERAL – THE STRUCTURE OF PERCEIVED VALUE.

The economy of the business world is set up in a natural order in which the supply of goods is manufactured based on the demand by the consumers in society. Within this structure an independent need outside the supply and demand of that particular product can be created. For example, there is a useful need in general industry for diamonds in all its various forms from pulverized powder to shaping for tools and use in computers. On the other hand, the rough diamond when fashioned into a finished gem diamond begs the question, was it based on supply and demand? Indeed, was the demand created through promotion and advertising and then the product produced to meet the ever promoted demand?

In whatever way we view the above, the structure of it is firmly in place, so much so that even those companies and mining groups that are outside of the inner circle will follow along with the general trend because their profit margins depend on holding the structure together.

Each gem quality rough diamond, whether individually or grouped together in a parcel is technically different than the other. Therefore, logical reasoning will assume that its value will also be different. The same can be said for each finished diamond. The distance between fashioning from rough to finished is considered man induced and is referred to as the cut or make. The cut adds considerable variance to the price of the finished diamond. However, since we have certain parameters that classify a certain type of color and clarity in which essentially are subjective, we can assume that we can indeed group together rough diamonds that fall within the range of a certain color and clarity. Added to this group is the size of each rough which is quantifiable in the present carat system of weighing.

To properly grasp value in rough diamonds, we shold understand that there are certain natural prerequisites that will automatically come into focus as a rough purchaser.

166

A. The expense of locating a geographic area in which rough diamonds can be profitably extracted. Added to this is the cost of license and permits that will need to be obtained.

B. The expense of moving equipment into position and carrying out the actual mining. The cost of equipment will be dependent on the type of mining and the type of deposit found.

C. The expense of transforming the rough diamond through cutting and polishing into a finished product. This area will have to consider if the diamond is to be sawed, bruted, cut and polished.

D. The expense of marketing the finished product for a profitable return. The cost of transportation, advertising and evaluation as a finished diamond are only some of the areas that will need to be considered.

The following guidelines will further clear the concept of value in rough diamonds.

2. EXAMINATION OF ROUGH DIAMONDS

A student may intellectually have all the knowledge imparted to him in the classroom but interpretation of that knowledge is even more important as he views rough diamonds and begins to access all the factors necessary to come up with a purchase price.

A. The standard magnification used in the field is a fully corrected 10x loupe. The lens should be kept clean and free from all dirt, dust and fingerprints. If you are right handed, the loupe should be held in the right hand and the rough diamond in the left hand by the thumb and index finger. In this manner the left hand is free to rotate the diamond in all directions for viewing. Both hands can touch each other and the elbows placed on a desk for steady observation. (photo 7.1)

7.1

B. The background for viewing most types of rough is preferably a flat white background with a daylight overhead lightsource. While out in the field a flat white paper background with indirect sunlight can be used.

C. It should be pointed out that the manner in which the diamond is rotated in the thumb and index finger is important to observing internal inclusions. A combination of the correct use of the light source and background to view inclusions especially difficult to detect inclusions, is a learned exercise requiring patience and practice.

3. VALUE IN RELATION TO INCLUSIONS.

To place a value based on the location of an inclusion, the question will have to be asked, "Can the inclusion be removed after manufacturing or will it remain?" If it remains, at what location in the finished diamond will it be situated? Upon making these types of decisions a final conservative clarity grade is assigned to the rough in which it may be used to deduce a final value of the rough.

168

The ability to judge the depth of an inclusion and possible removal require a combination of knowledge that is taught during the rough diamond grading program at A.I.D.C. Inc.

4. VALUE IN RELATION TO COLOR.

When value is ascribed to rough diamonds based on color, it should be understood that the observer's view of color is based not only on the correct method of observation but the observer's experience with that type of rough from that particular location. Color plays only one part in a series of judgment that will have to be made in the evaluation of a rough diamond. (Refer to chapter five for an understanding of color conditions)

5. VALUE IN RELATION TO EXPECTED WEIGHT RECOVERY.

One of the single most important factors in determining value in rough diamonds is the comparison of its rough weight to its completed weight after manufacturing. Why is this so important? Without an understanding of the weight recovery, gross errors in determining the final purchase price will be made.

Any single rough diamond or an entire parcel will have to be analyzed based on the shape of the cut. Is it going to be a round brilliant or a fancy cut and what final weight will the rough yield? Therefore, insight to the diameter of the rough in relation to its depth will be necessary to assess weight recovery, combined with the shape of cut and proportions projected from the given rough.

The symmetry and shape of the rough often determines whether a single rough will produce two finished diamonds or one single diamond. Understanding the outward structure as well as the internal structure and then combining the two to produce the highest weight yield which will result in the greatest value.

6. VALUE IN RELATION TO CUT.

It cannot be understated on how profound an impact cut has in relation to the value of the rough diamond. First let us examine very briefly the issue of cut.

At the writing of this chapter the entire industry is taking a good hard look at the long over due issue of cut. It may be many more years before some type of agreeable understanding exists in the industry. The heart of the issue with regard to cut is the finished diamond proportions and resultant fire and brilliance observed in the face up position. This of course can vary from one diamond to the other especially in the fancy shapes. Let us look at some practical issues related to cut and clarity.

A. Inclusions – Determining the feasibility of removing an inclusion by manufacturing the rough diamond with proportions that are less than ideal to increase the value of the finished diamond. Another aspect would be to manufacture the rough other than in a standard shape or choosing a fancy cut over a round brilliant to remove a major inclusion thereby increasing the value of the finished diamond.

B. Color – This area is not often affected by cut. However, due to the size of finished diamonds from the same rough, color can be as much as several grades different. This is the result of a larger finished diamond being able to draw more color than a smaller one. Another area would be fancy colors. Certain colors in rough diamonds that are not saturated enough to be considered true fancy colors can be cut and polished to increase the saturation of color thereby increasing the value of the finished diamond.

C. Weight Class – A rough diamond after manufacturing yields a weight of 0.95ct. with very good proportions. Would this be considered the best yield in weight for the diamond? A rough buyer that understands the diamond market will prefer to have the rough manufactured with less than good proportions and thereby obtain a finished diamond of 1.00ct. which in most cases will command a higher value than the 0.95ct. Finishing the diamond in a weight class above or below one carat will make a difference in value. The above are only some aspects with regard to value in relation to cut that will be explored in the classroom.

7. MARKET FLUCATIONS.

Understanding the general diamond market and price fluctuations that occurs from time to time becomes advantageous when marketing the finished diamond as well as purchasing rough diamonds. Certain sizes that will produce finished goods in particular colors, clarity and cut will command premium prices because of the scarcity and demand for these type of goods. For this to occur, the availability of rough diamonds in these qualities were not available in sufficient quantity to meet the market demand.

Another area that usually cause price fluctuations is when the demand exist for certain fancy shapes or matched sizes in certain cuts. Matched sizes not only mean two pieces but can literally mean matched sizes in hundreds of pieces to set in a particular jewelry piece. Graduated sizes can also command higher prices.

Because of market conditions in certain qualities and sizes the finished diamond can be sold readily if it is accompanied with a grading report from a recognized laboratory. Understanding when to grade a finished diamond to maximize its selling potential is important to increasing its market value.

8. SUMMARY

We can now clearly see that all aspects of the rough will have to be considered simultaneously and then a given price can be reached. All areas such as color, clarity, rough weight, projected cut and final finished weight will need to be linked together to arrive at the market value with profit margins factored in as well.

The actual fixing of purchase price on rough diamonds is taught in the classroom for both single rough pieces and parcels by a qualified instructor. Included in this instruction is the pricing and grading of industrial rough and its place relative to gem rough.

All areas outlined in this chapter are placed in perspective and a formula that takes into consideration all the differentials including a margin of profit will be taken into account.

Rough Diamonds, "A Practical Guide", is the first work of its kind ever completed. It is an authoritative and concise guide on the subject of rough diamonds. When combined with studies in the classroom, it equips the student with essential knowledge to step with confidence into the field of rough diamond purchasing.

ABOUT THE AUTHOR

Mr. Nizam Peters is founder, director and senior instructor of the American Institute of Diamond Cutting, Inc. An internationally recognized school dedicated to teaching the art of diamond cutting and rough diamond grading.

Mr. Peters has spent over twenty five productive years in the diamond industry, his experience extends to field operations in the mining, recovery and purchasing of rough diamond both in the industrial and gem quality sector. The author has spent many years in developing technologically advanced diamond cutting machines in which he has been granted international patents. His diamond cutting ability has earned him the reputation for cutting and polishing unusual shapes and difficult rough. Over a five year period, Mr. Peters has personally selected and photographed each diamond that appears in this book.

Mr. Peters is also the author/photographer of the popular field guide, "Rough diamonds, Internal and External Features."

The author personally teaches the rough diamond grading program and is available for consultation, field trips and appraising of rough diamonds.

ISBN 0-9665854-1-0   9000

9 780966 585414

Printed in Colombia